World Geography

World Weather

climate & climatic change

Atlantic Europe Publishing

How to use this book

There are many ways of using this book. Below you will see how each page is arranged to help you to find information quickly, revise main ideas or look for material in detail. The choice is yours!

On some pages you will find words that have been shown in CAPITALS. There is a full explanation of each of these words in the glossary on page 63.

This heading in the running text tells you about the section that follows.

This is the main column of running text that forms the chapter. Read this for a good understanding of the subject as a whole.

Scan these boxes for key ideas.

The information in the box describes an important subject in detail and gives additional facts.

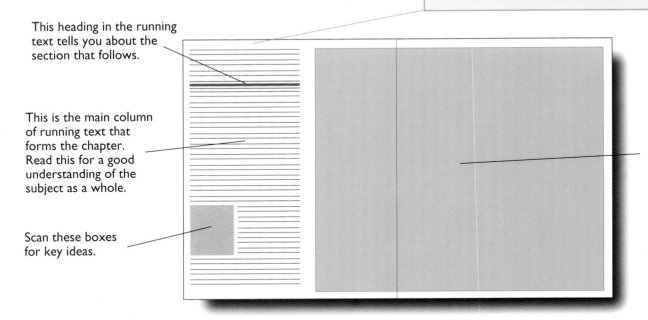

Author
Brian Knapp, BSc, PhD
Educational Consultant
Stephen Codrington, BA, DipEd, PhD
Art Director
Duncan McCrae, BSc
Editor
Elizabeth Walker, BA
Illustrators
David Woodroffe and Tim Smith
Designed and produced by
EARTHSCAPE EDITIONS
Print consultants
Landmark Production Consultants Ltd
Printed and bound by
Paramount Printing Company Ltd

First published in the United Kingdom in 1995 by Atlantic Europe Publishing Company Limited, 86 Peppard Road, Sonning Common, Reading, Berkshire, RG4 9RP, UK

The Atlantic Europe Publishing logo is a registered trademark of Atlantic Europe Publishing Company Limited.

Suggested cataloguing location

Knapp, Brian
World weather, climate and climatic change
– (World Geography; 11)
551.6

ISBN 1-869860-83-7

Acknowledgements
The publishers would like to thank the following for their help and advice: *Aspen Flying Club*, Englewood, Colorado; *Bridgeford Flying Service*, Napa, California; *The Royal Commonwealth Society Collection, the Syndics of Cambridge University Library*, Cambridge, UK; *Oxfam*, India; *Oxfam*, Kenya; *David Newell, Oxfam-Bridge*, Thailand.

Picture credits
(c=centre t=top b=bottom l=left r=right)
All photographs are from the **Earthscape Editions** library except the following: **British Petroleum Company plc** 2cr, 60/61, 61tr; by permission of **the Syndics of Cambridge University Library** 22/23; **Stephen Codrington** 36/37; **University of Dundee** 58bl; **NASA** 6cl, 24; **USGS** 25br.

This product is manufactured from sustainable managed forests. For every tree cut down at least one more is planted.

Contents

Chapter 1
Facts about weather and climate 5
Energy for the weather machine 6
The Earth in balance 6
The atmosphere 7
Where weather occurs 8
Thermals and winds 8
The causes of wind 8
Wind speeds 9
The effects of land and sea 10
The influence of oceans 10
Oceans and climate 11
Moisture in the air 12
Clouds, rain and snow 12
Cumulus clouds 14
Rain and snow 16
Types of cloud 16
Layer clouds 16
Weather forecasting 18
Weather of hills and mountains 18
Forecasting around the world 20

Chapter 2
Weather hazards and disasters 23
Severe winds 24
Extreme events 26
Sudden disasters 26
Severe rain and floods 26
Prolonged disasters 28
El Niño: a global weather disaster 28
Hazards of ignorance 30
Modern hazards 30
Fog 30
Forecasting severe weather events 32
Smog 32

Chapter 3
Climate, the past and the future 35
Climate clues from the past 36
The Earth's climate today 36
Climate changes that could have
  affected history 36
People v Earth – who is in control of the
  climate? 38
Are we altering the world's climate? 38
Global warming: the Greenhouse
  Effect 39

Chapter 4
A guide to the world's climates 41
The humid tropics 41
Tropical rainforest climate 42
Monsoon 44
Dry climates 44
The seasons of the tropics 44
The Indian monsoon 45
Savanna climate 46
Dry mid-latitude steppe
  and prairie climates 48
Arid and semi-arid climates 48
Steppe and prairie climate 50
Humid mid-latitude climates 52
Subtropical (warm temperate) climate 52
The jet streams 54
Mediterranean climate 54
The battle between cool and warm air 56
Cool temperate rainy climates 56
Humid cold climates 58
Polar climates 58
Highs and lows 58
Depression weather 59
How the North and South Poles differ 60
Weather in cold lands: northern North
  America and Siberia 60
Mountain climates 62

Glossary 63

Index 64

Chapter I

Facts about weather and climate

The atmosphere – the air around us – is a mixture of invisible gases. It is affected by heat from the Sun, the oceans and the continents. It is also affected by the way the Earth spins.

Differences in the heating of the atmosphere, combined with the spinning of the Earth, set in place great swirling patterns of air that give the cloud and rain patterns of day-to-day life and that, from time to time, are powerful enough to demolish houses, and cause floods, blizzards or droughts.

Weather is a word we use to describe the way the ATMOSPHERE changes day by day. We notice this, for example, as changes in warmth, cloudiness, wind speed and rainfall. The day-to-day movement of air is seen in the way the clouds change, how the temperature rises and falls, whether it is windy or calm, or whether it is dry or wet. The weather affects such immediate things as what we might wear each day.

Over many years, however, the everyday changes blend into a long-term pattern which we can describe with numbers, or STATISTICS.

❏ (left) Blue skies highlight the magnificence of the Dolomite Mountains after a recent snowfall. Why should the weather change so quickly? The answer lies in the way invisible currents of air move through the atmosphere.

These statistics help us to determine the *climate* of a place. The climate affects more long-term issues such as what crops we grow, how we build our houses and how much energy we have to use to keep ourselves warm or cool. It also affects the way plants grow, the behaviour of animals and how the landscape is ERODED.

Energy for the weather machine

To understand how the atmosphere moves, why it is hot and cold, windy and calm, and why it sometimes rains, we need to look at the way air moves over the Earth.

You can think of the way the air moves about as something like the workings of a complicated machine. The energy that powers the weather machine comes from the Sun. The Sun shines directly near the Equator, making the land and oceans hot, whereas it shines at a slanting angle (more obliquely) towards the poles and so has a much smaller heating effect.

> The weather machine is driven by extra heating within the tropics. This sets the atmosphere in motion and creates the patterns of weather all over the globe.

Because the atmosphere is a gas which is free to move, or circulate, these contrasts in temperature cause air to flow from the tropics to the poles. This is what 'powers' the global CIRCULATION of the air.

All parts of the Earth are linked by the global circulation. This is why a change in one part of the world will, in time, also affect all other parts of the world's atmosphere. Some people have called it the 'butterfly effect', meaning that the smallest movement of air caused by the flapping of the wings of a butterfly anywhere in the world, might set in motion a chain of events that would eventually be felt across the entire world.

The Earth in balance

In the long term the Earth is not getting hotter or colder, so the same amount of energy must be lost from the Earth as it gains from the Sun: it is a matter of balancing the energy books.

The Sun, which is enormously hot (about 6000°C), sends out, or radiates, energy into space. A tiny amount of this reaches the Earth. The atmosphere absorbs very little of this energy and so the land and sea receive most of the heat.

The Sun's radiation is obvious to us because we can feel its heat directly. But although the Earth warms up a little, it never gets above about 40°C. This is because radiation is continually lost from all parts of the Earth to balance the heat received from the Sun.

One way to think of the relationship between the energy sent out and received by the Sun and the Earth is to compare them with a central heating system: the Sun acts as the white-hot flames of a boiler, the Earth as one vast radiator which, after a small delay, gives out as much heat as the boiler puts in. As a result, the Earth never warms up enough to glow like the Sun.

❒ (below) The pattern of air currents is made complex by the spinning motion of the Earth. Compare a picture of the Earth taken from space with the diagram that shows the basic air movements on the right.

❒ (right) In this picture taken from a jet aircraft, the troposphere is the thin white zone on the horizon; the clear blue sky above it is the stratosphere.

The atmosphere

In terms of weather and climate, the most important layers of the atmosphere are closest to the ground. The layer containing all the clouds is the troposphere (tropo means 'turning over'; this part of the atmosphere is continually turning over). Above it is another layer called the stratosphere (strato means 'layer', so stratosphere means the layered (unchanging) part of the atmosphere). The stratosphere acts as an atmospheric 'lid', keeping all the overturning air and cloud relatively close to the ground.

Much of the Sun's energy gets through the layers of gases of the atmosphere and warms the oceans and the land. The warmed Earth in turn radiates energy to space. But two gases in the troposphere – carbon dioxide and water vapour – trap some of the heat, helping to warm the air near the ground.

The amount of water and carbon dioxide in the air vary from time to time and from place to place. In recent centuries, human activity has added considerable amounts of carbon dioxide to the air, causing it to store more heat than it might otherwise do. This is called the Greenhouse Effect.

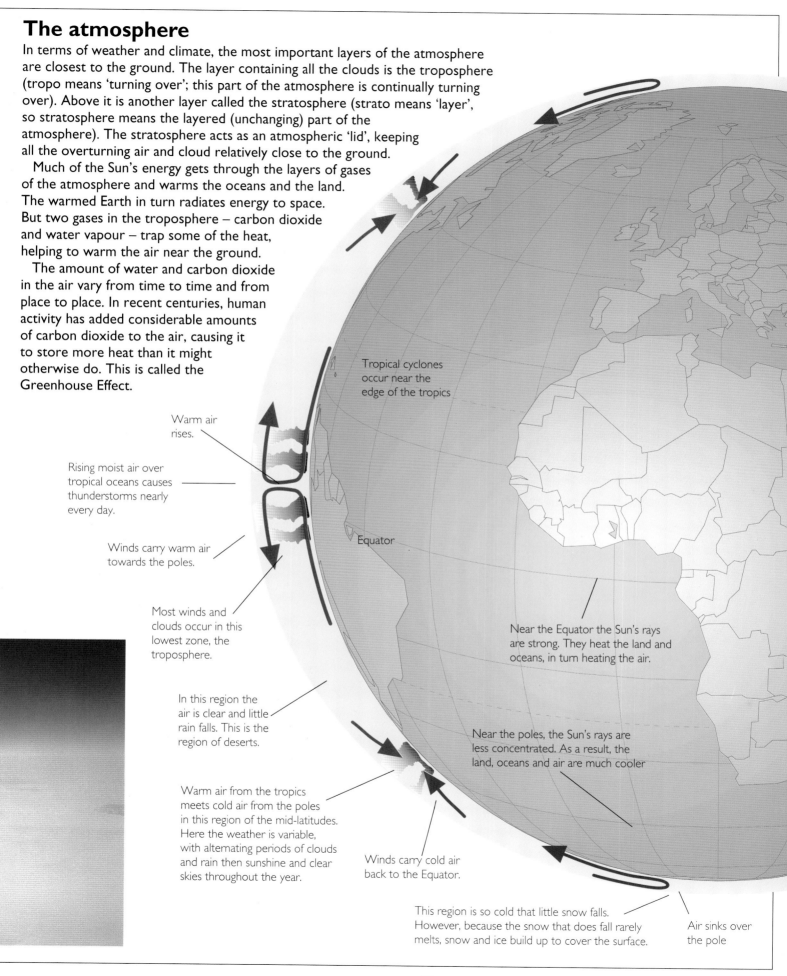

Tropical cyclones occur near the edge of the tropics

Warm air rises.

Rising moist air over tropical oceans causes thunderstorms nearly every day.

Winds carry warm air towards the poles.

Most winds and clouds occur in this lowest zone, the troposphere.

Equator

In this region the air is clear and little rain falls. This is the region of deserts.

Warm air from the tropics meets cold air from the poles in this region of the mid-latitudes. Here the weather is variable, with alternating periods of clouds and rain then sunshine and clear skies throughout the year.

Winds carry cold air back to the Equator.

Near the Equator the Sun's rays are strong. They heat the land and oceans, in turn heating the air.

Near the poles, the Sun's rays are less concentrated. As a result, the land, oceans and air are much cooler

This region is so cold that little snow falls. However, because the snow that does fall rarely melts, snow and ice build up to cover the surface.

Air sinks over the pole

Where weather occurs

The Earth is enclosed within a very thick 'shell' of air – the atmosphere – but most 'weather' is produced close to the Earth's surface. This lowest part of the atmosphere, from the ground up to between 8 and 16 km, is known as the troposphere, and it contains nearly all of the world's clouds.

> Air moves across the globe from high to low-pressure regions. Some (trade) winds in the tropics blow constantly, because the highs and lows change little throughout the year; by contrast, those in mid-latitudes change from day to day.

If you fly in an aircraft on a long-distance journey you can usually see the top of the troposphere clearly because most aircraft fly in the cloudless layer above and you can look down onto the clouds. This layer, which acts like a lid, keeping the clouds in the air below, is called the stratosphere.

Thermals and winds

The Sun does not directly heat the lower part of the air. In fact the troposphere is almost completely transparent to sunshine. This is why we feel the direct warmth of the Sun on a cloudless day. Clouds do not absorb much heat either, but they do reflect sunshine back to space, so that places with lots of cloud tend to have cooler weather than those that are cloudless.

The air becomes warmed indirectly. First the Sun heats up the land and the oceans. The air then gets its heat by contact (conduction) with the land and water. The air also absorbs heat radiated from the land and water. As a result the air is heated from below, not from above. This is of great importance because it means that the air is heated at the base, just like the bottom of a saucepan of liquid when it is heated on a stove.

The causes of wind

There are three different groups of winds:

Worldwide winds, like the Trade Winds and the Westerlies, blow over large areas of the world. In the mid-latitudes, for example, there is almost always a wind blowing with speeds between 20 and 50 km per hour.

Worldwide winds are caused by the circulation of air between the tropics and the poles. Westerly winds are produced by air flowing *from* the tropics to the poles, whereas easterly 'trade' winds are produced by air flowing *towards* the tropics.

Regional winds are often connected to some special feature of land or sea. They are caused by local changes in temperature or in pressure within the atmosphere, and they blow between high and low-pressure regions in the mid-latitudes. For example, MONSOON winds occur when moist warm air rushes onto land.

Local winds tend to occur over quite small areas when the atmosphere is calm, for example, mountain and valley winds and sea breezes. As air flows over mountains, it is forced to rise; on the far side of the mountains it can sink again. Winds are created on both sides of mountains, but the best known are the sinking winds, such as the Foehn wind of the Alps or the Chinook of North America.

Sea breezes which occur when the land is warmer than the sea are called onshore breezes; when the sea is warmer than the land they are called offshore breezes.

❏ (above) The wispy cirrus clouds seen over this mountain range show the direction of high-level winds that would otherwise be invisible.

❐ (left) Constant fierce winds that blow during the winters in the South Pacific cause these macrocarpa trees to grow in a contorted way.

Wind speeds

In some areas, such as the part of the world known to sailors as the Doldrums, the air is usually calm. In these places, air near the Earth's surface moves more slowly than the air aloft, because the rough ground acts as a brake. Winds blow most strongly over the oceans and plains, because there is less drag from the Earth.

Near the top of the troposphere, winds may be over 100 km per hour, and in some narrow zones – known as jet streams – they may exceed 300 km per hour.

Winds on the ground become strong only when the air begins to spin. Just like skaters begin to spin with arms outstretched, and then pull them in to spin faster, spinning air can develop very high speeds. In tropical cyclones winds can reach over 200 km per hour, but the fastest winds occur in tornadoes, where they can reach several hundred kilometres an hour.

Winds and pressure

As air moves across the surface of the Earth, it tends to pile up in some places more than others. Places where the air is piled up can be seen using a BAROMETER. This shows that in such places the air pressure is high. By contrast there are places where the amount of air is much less. The barometer shows these to be regions of low pressure.

Air always flows out of places with high pressure to places of low pressure, creating wind. The closer high and low-pressure regions are to each other, the faster the air flows.

On a weather chart, the air pressure is shown by lines called isobars. Where the isobars are close together, the change from high to low pressure is very fast and the winds are at their strongest. This is why weather forecasters use pressure maps to find the regions of strong winds.

❐ (right) A region of low pressure over eastern Australia is clearly picked out by patterns of isobars. Winds blow from the regions of high pressure to regions of low pressure.

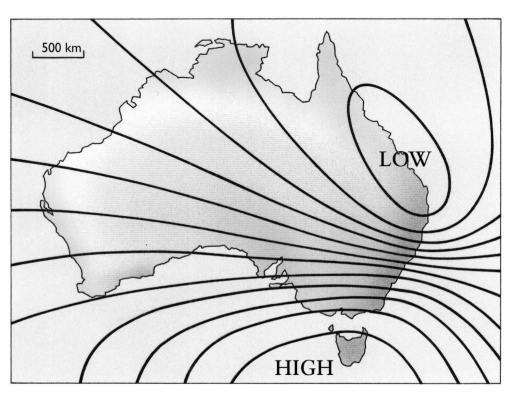

500 km

LOW

HIGH

When any fluid (either a gas like air or a liquid like the oceans) is heated, the hot fluid swells and becomes less dense. So, like a bubble rising from the bottom of a heated saucepan, as soon as air is warmed it rises through the colder air above. Sometimes you can see the hot air as a kind of shimmering

> The oceans transfer as much heat from the tropics to other parts of the Earth as all of the world's winds. They also heat up and cool down very slowly through the year, so that here changes from summer to winter are less dramatic than near the centre of a continent.

over land and roads on a hot day. This is the shimmering that also causes MIRAGES. You can also see the effect of heating indirectly because it is responsible for the formation of cumulus cloud (see page 12). Each of these 'pillow-like' clouds is a rising column of air called a thermal, and they are strong enough that birds and glider aircraft can use them to gain height.

So, because the air is heated from below it is always turning over. At night the heating effect of the Sun ceases and there are fewer thermals rising (and less cumulus cloud).

Around the Earth, the rising air in the tropics pushes out towards the poles near the top of the troposphere, and the cold air of the poles is forced out towards the tropics. This flow is responsible for most of the world's winds.

The effects of land and sea

The continents have a dramatic influence on the weather. This is because heat from the Sun is only stored in the top metre or so of the soil and rock. On a hot sunny day the land surface becomes very hot, causing daily cloud and

The influence of oceans

Although when we swim in some oceans they may feel cold, in fact they transfer as much heat from the tropics to the mid-latitudes and poles as all the winds that blow.

The reason is that, unlike land where only the surface heats up, the Sun's rays filter as far as 100 m below the ocean surface. However, when the Sun is at a low angle in the sky, it acts like a giant mirror, reflecting almost all of the Sun's rays. As a result, ocean waters in high latitudes are poorly heated.

The great contrast between heat received and stored by the oceans in the tropics and in high latitudes causes ocean currents. Warm waters travel near the surface and returning waters move at depth. Movement of ocean water is affected by the spinning Earth, causing water to swing to the right of its path in the northern hemisphere and to the left in the southern hemisphere.

Worldwide winds, like the Trade Winds, also have a part to play. For example, the northeasterly Trade Winds help transfer water from the coast of Africa, across the Atlantic where it adds to the Gulf of Mexico.

Warm currents tend to form well defined threads within otherwise cold water. The Gulf Stream/North Atlantic Drift is perhaps the best known of these. Both warm and cold currents have an important effect on climate. Westerlies blowing over the North Atlantic Drift, for example, are warmed; they, in turn, bring mild weather to northwestern Europe.

❐ (below) Many of the world's permanent pasturelands are created by warm moist airstreams bringing reliable rainfall throughout the year.

Water sinks near the poles.

Warm water flows poleward.

Cold water returns.

The effects of heat transfer around the oceans

Water warmed in the tropics.

Humid forest climates occur here.

Coastal deserts occur here.

❐ (above) As oceans receive more heat from the Sun in the tropics than near the poles, warm water flows from the tropics to the poles. This diagram applies to the Northern Hemisphere.

(left) The famous fog that hugs the coasts of northern California in summer is produced where a cold ocean current wells up just off the shore. The sea cools the air and produces fogs that last for many months. (The fog is drawn onshore every day by sea breezes.)

Oceans and climate

There is a constant exchange of heat between the air and the oceans. As a result, those lands bordering oceans often have a much more even temperature throughout the year than places in the centre of continents. Coastal locations are said to have a 'maritime climate'. Those inland have a 'continental climate'.

A warm current (such as the North Atlantic Drift that flows from the Gulf of Mexico to Europe) warms the air and makes the climate mild.

Cold water usually flows back to the tropics along the eastern side near the bottom of the ocean.

Where a cold current flows along the coast (such as in California) air is cooled and fog is common.

Warm ocean currents usually flow along the western side of the ocean basin, near the surface.

Rivers get their water from the moisture-laden winds that blow from the oceans. This is why areas with onshore winds are humid, support forests and are usually good for farming. Those with offshore winds tend to be deserts.

thunderstorms. But because little heat is stored, in the evening the land cools down quickly and the clouds melt away.

In the mid and high latitudes, the fact that land cannot store heat produces great contrasts between summer (when the Sun is more nearly overhead) and winter (when it reaches only a low angle). The result is that places near the centres of continents experience large differences from season to season.

This difference also affects rain and snowfall. Areas in the centres of continents have most of their rain (as thunderstorms) in the summer; the winters are cold and dry.

> As air rises, it cools and can contain less moisture. It is then more likely to form clouds.

By contrast, oceans can soak up heat in their deep surface layers. This means that they do not change temperature as rapidly from day to day. Thunderstorms can easily continue by day as well as night over hot oceans. The most feared of all are the tropical thunderstorms, or tropical cyclones, that are called hurricanes and typhoons. They use the energy of the heat and the moisture from the oceans to fuel their ferocious spiralling winds.

Because oceans do not lose heat as quickly as the land, changes happen gradually over the seasons. Cloud and rain can be formed over oceans (and spread to the land nearby) during the winter season, as well as in summer, when the centres of the continents are cold and dry throughout the winter.

Moisture in the air

Many of the features of the weather depend on the amount of moisture in the air. The air contains moisture both as an invisible gas called water vapour, and as water droplets in the form of cloud, rain or fog, or as ice crystals (snow). When the air is cooled, water vapour changes to the droplets that produce clouds, and rain or snow occurs.

Clouds, rain and snow

Clouds contain vast numbers of tiny water droplets and sometimes ice crystals as well. Each droplet or ice crystal has formed by condensing on dust and other tiny airborne particles. They are so small that they can be kept in the air by the lightest of breezes.

Ice is rare in warm tropical clouds; it usually forms only in very cold clouds. In the mid and high latitudes, clouds may have water droplets in their lower levels and ice crystals near their tops. Most rain that forms from stratus (layer) clouds actually starts as snow and melts on the way down. If it doesn't melt, snow falls.

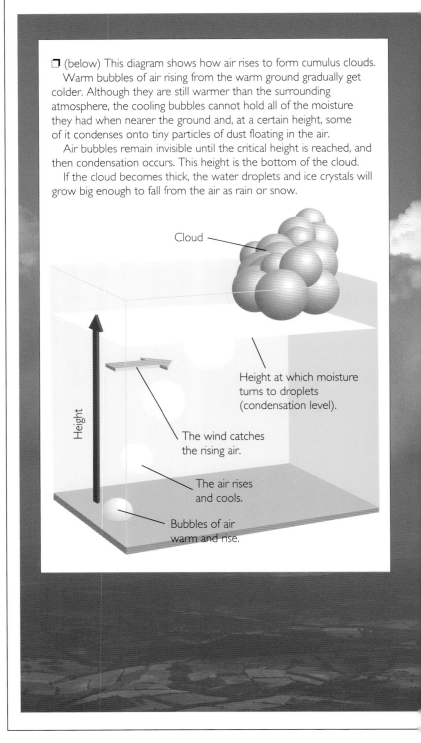

❏ (below) This diagram shows how air rises to form cumulus clouds.
Warm bubbles of air rising from the warm ground gradually get colder. Although they are still warmer than the surrounding atmosphere, the cooling bubbles cannot hold all of the moisture they had when nearer the ground and, at a certain height, some of it condenses onto tiny particles of dust floating in the air.

Air bubbles remain invisible until the critical height is reached, and then condensation occurs. This height is the bottom of the cloud.

If the cloud becomes thick, the water droplets and ice crystals will grow big enough to fall from the air as rain or snow.

Cloud

Height

Height at which moisture turns to droplets (condensation level).

The wind catches the rising air.

The air rises and cools.

Bubbles of air warm and rise.

Cumulus clouds, rain and hail

The different amounts of water and ice in a cloud are critical to the way that rain forms. In tropical cumulus clouds, thermals can be very strong and water droplets may have to be very large before they can fall. But strong air currents actually sweep the droplets together until they become large enough to fall from the cloud. This explains why tropical rain is made of large droplets.

Sometimes droplets are carried rapidly up and down inside a cloud by the fierce thermals. As they reach the cloud top they begin to freeze, and get a coating of ice (called rime); then they are forced rapidly downward, gathering a coating of more small water droplets before being carried aloft once more where the surface water again freezes. After several cycles, large HAILSTONES may form this way, sometimes reaching the size of golf balls or even oranges.

Stratus clouds and rain

In the mid-latitudes, only summer thunderstorms have the fierce thermals that drag droplets together to make large raindrops. In most layer clouds, the currents of rising air are much weaker and a different rain-making process is at work.

By making some of the world's first high-level aircraft flights in the 1920s, the Norwegian scientist Bergeron discovered how rain, sleet and snow all form from a single process.

During his flights he found that water droplets get lifted up into the upper regions of a cloud where ice crystals occur. In this zone the water droplets help provide the moisture needed to make ice crystals grow big enough to form large snowflakes which then fall from the cloud. If the air below the cloud is warm, the snowflakes melt and the cloud produces droplets of rain. If the air is cold, then the crystals do not melt and the clouds produce snow, or partly melted snow called sleet.

Most water droplets are so small they cannot be seen with the naked eye, even in the densest fog. To be seen they have to group together into larger droplets. To see some larger droplets make a hot steaming beverage and put it in front of a light. You will see the water particles steaming off the beverage. Here they are carried upwards because the air above the beverage is hot and, just like a hot-air balloon, it rises.

The steaming air is lost to sight just a few centimetres above the beverage because the air around it is dry. The droplets simply evaporate into the warm dry air.

Very little air movement is needed to keep such tiny drops suspended, forever out of reach of the ground, and it is all too easy for them to evaporate back to vapour. Clearly not all moisture forms clouds and clouds do not automatically give rain or snow.

> Clouds form two groups: those that develop bubbly shapes – known as cumulus clouds – and those that develop as sheets or layers – called stratus and cirrus clouds.

It takes about a million cloud droplets or ice crystals to make one small raindrop or the beginnings of one small snowflake. But the droplets do not easily join to each other, Instead they need to settle out onto tiny pieces of 'dust' in the air. This process is called condensation.

You can often see the tiny pieces of dust floating in a beam of sunlight in a room. The dust is made of pieces of soil, tiny crystals of salt and many other things, including particles of soot from chimneys and vehicle exhausts. Water vapour condenses and forms droplets around this dust. Each particle gets coated with water until it is big enough to fall out of the air. You can sometimes see the dust after a brief rainshower in a city as dirty marks on clean surfaces after the rain has evaporated.

Cumulus clouds

Cumulus clouds are individual clouds that form when warm air rises. They may form patterns of small clouds (often called pillow clouds) or even high-level patterns consisting of thousands of tiny clouds (forming a 'mackerel sky'). Under suitable conditions, and particularly in the tropics or interiors of continents in summer, they may also form giant towering thunderclouds, known as cumulonimbus clouds.

The pattern of cumulus clouds tells how air is behaving in the sky. There is always a balance between rising and sinking air. Clouds occur where warm air is rising; clear patches show where air is sinking. With giant thunderstorms, the cool sinking air provides very strong winds at ground level.

❐ (above and below) These are 'fair-weather' cumulus clouds. They will not grow into thunderclouds.

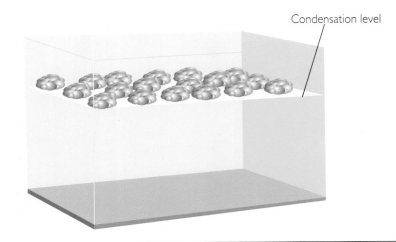

Condensation level

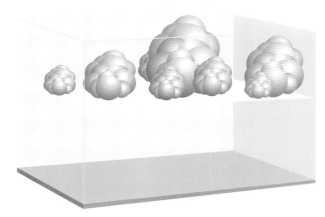

❏ (below) This diagram shows how cumulus clouds build up. Every cloud may have many thermals inside, each trying to push higher. This is what causes the bubbly or 'turreted' top to the clouds. Turrets that are actively growing show that the thermals are powerful and that the air above them is fresh and cold. These clouds will probably thicken enough to produce showers during the day.

❏ (above) This picture shows the top of a large, growing cumulus cloud. This cloud may produce light showers, but it is not yet a thundercloud.

The development of rain-bearing cumulus clouds

Rain-bearing cumulus clouds are called cumulonimbus clouds (pictures right and below). They typically begin to billow up on a hot morning, their towers gradually building until they dominate the sky. The great height to which they grow shows that they contain very strong updraughts, or thermals.

These clouds produce thunder and lightning. Lightning (and the sound of the lightning flash, thunder) is produced as strong thermals cause water droplets to brush against each other. This brushing effect gradually builds up an electric charge. Lightning cannot develop in thinner clouds, because the updraughts are not great enough to cause water droplets to brush against each other.

Rain and snow

The smallest raindrops to reach the ground, (as drizzle) are about a tenth of a millimetre across, and 'true' raindrops are usually over 1 mm in diameter. Even the smallest raindrops reaching the ground must be over ten times the size of the average cloud droplet, so there must be a way that droplets can grow large enough to fall as rain or snow. This happens in one of two ways: one way works inside thunderclouds, especially in the tropics, and may produce deluges as well as hailstorms; the other way occurs in cold clouds away from the tropics where both water droplets and ice crystals occur. This produces long periods of steady rain or snow. This is shown in detail on page 13.

> Rain and snow can only form around tiny particles of dust in the air. If more rain is needed, aircraft sometimes scatter dust made of special chemicals to encourage condensation. This is called 'cloud seeding'.

Types of cloud

There are two basic shapes of cloud: Individual clouds with a puffy or billowing shape are called cumulus-type clouds. They form when the ground is heated in some places more than others, so that the air rises in an irregular way. Clouds that form as sheets to make a layer are known as stratus-type clouds. They form when air is lifted up in a uniform way.

Each type of cloud can also be identified by its height:

☛ If the clouds are of middle height they are given the name alto (for example altostratus, for middle-level layer clouds).

Layer clouds

Layer clouds are of two types: the thin wispy veils of ice crystals called cirrus clouds, and the thicker cloud sheets of water droplets (and perhaps ice crystals) called stratus clouds. Rain-bearing stratus clouds are called nimbostratus. There are few swift thermals in these clouds, and thunder and lightning rarely occur.

Layer clouds are rarely found in the hot tropics, but are mostly typical of mid and high latitudes. They provide the bulk of the clouds that form around depressions, and they are also quite commonly found where flows of air are forced up over hills, mountains or coastal cliffs.

❐ (left and below) This picture and diagram show thin, high stratus cloud. Notice how the cloud is patchy in the foreground, but changes to a sheet in the background. This marks the onset of a depression.
(See diagram at right and also page 58 for more on DEPRESSIONS.)

Layer clouds and mid-latitude depressions

Layer clouds are most commonly found in mid-latitude depressions, where warm air from tropical regions meets cold air from polar areas. The colder air is heavier than the warm air, and it flows under it, pushing the warm air off the ground. The warm air begins to cool as it lifts off the ground, and eventually layer clouds form.

The highest, thinnest clouds are called cirrostratus; those at mid-height are called altostratus, while the thickest, rain-bearing clouds are nimbostratus clouds.

A larger, more detailed version of this diagram, and a longer explanation of the weather in a depression is given on page 58.

□ (main picture) The heavy, dark nimbus clouds on the right have produced rain. They mark the trailing edge of the cold front of a depression (position E). The cloud is continuing to move right, allowing clear, colder air to follow.

☛ If the clouds are at high level they are give the name cirro (for example cirrostratus for high-level layer clouds).

☛ If they are low-level clouds, no extra word is added.

☛ If the clouds are thick, grey, leaden looking and rain-bearing, they are given the word nimbus or nimbo (for example cumulonimbus clouds are individual thick thunderstorm clouds).

Weather forecasting

Weather forecasting is the very practical and important business of giving people a reasonably accurate idea about the weather ahead. Knowing how moisture turns to clouds and rain is the key to explaining how the atmosphere works, and this in turn is the secret to predicting, or forecasting, the weather.

> If we know how the air is moving and how much moisture it holds, we can work out the chances of cloud and rain. Most forecasting still depends on reports from ground stations on temperature, pressure, wind and rain.

For centuries weather forecasting was a matter of recognising that certain types of cloud were related to certain types of weather. For example, thin cloud that gradually thickens marks the arrival of a DEPRESSION, and thus the chance of rain. Such ideas were behind folk sayings like "Red sky at night, shepherd's delight; red sky in the morning, shepherd's warning".

The most important advance in weather forecasting happened in the 19th century with the invention of the telegraph. Observers were able to send in reports from wide-ranging places, which then led to the building of weather charts.

Weather of hills and mountains

Hills and mountains produce their own kind of weather – wetter on the exposed (windward) and drier on the sheltered (leeward) side.

As air flows towards mountains it is forced to rise and cool. On the windward side of mountains, cooling air eventually has to shed some of its moisture. As a result the windward side of mountains are often masked in cloud even when the surrounding land has clear skies. This mountain rain, called *relief rain*, is <u>extra</u> rain – that is, in addition to the rain that might occur elsewhere in the area.

On the leeward side of the mountains, the air sinks and warms. As a result it can hold all of the remaining moisture, and the clouds formed on the windward side of the mountains evaporate. The leeward side is often called the *rainshadow region*, because it will rain much less here.

In some areas, especially those close to very high mountains, the mountains may force so much water from the air that almost none is left for the lowland beyond. In these cases a desert forms. The 'rainshadow deserts' in the southwestern United States, and in Argentina and Chile are examples of this kind of extreme effect.

❐ (above) This picture of the Southern Alps, near Mt Tasman, shows how clouds form over mountains, but then thin leaving clear skies beyond. The winds are blowing from right to left; the left-hand side is the rainshadow area.

Mountain and valley winds

When the atmosphere is calm, mountains cause their own local winds to form. At night, for example, the upper slopes of the mountains lose heat quickly and the air in contact with them gets cold, but in sheltered valleys the air remains quite warm. Cold air is heavier than warm air, so the cold mountain air rolls down into the valleys.

By morning this process may have filled the valleys with cold air. This can make mountain valleys very frost-prone and explains why many crops, such as fruit trees, are grown on the slopes, not on the valley floors.

Mountains can also produce winds that affect the surrounding plains when air piles up on one side of the mountains. In these cases, air can sometimes break out across the mountains and flow into the distant plains, at the same time perhaps sinking by a thousand metres or more. This sinking makes the air warm up and dry out. Warm winds such as the Foehn of the Alps and the Chinook of North America last for many days.

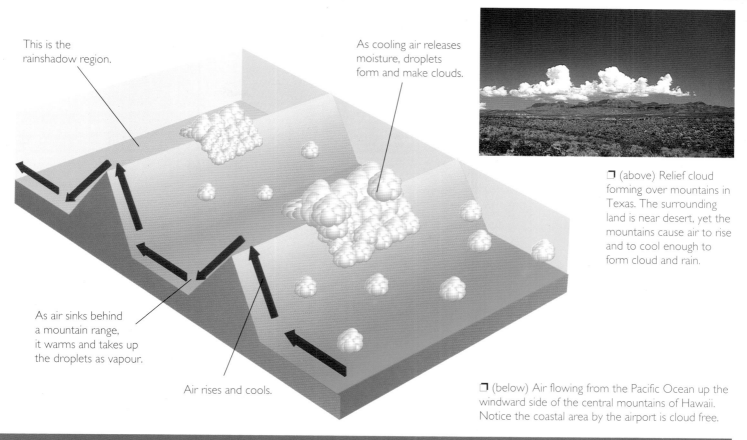

This is the
rainshadow region.

As cooling air releases
moisture, droplets
form and make clouds.

As air sinks behind
a mountain range,
it warms and takes up
the droplets as vapour.

Air rises and cools.

❒ (above) Relief cloud
forming over mountains in
Texas. The surrounding
land is near desert, yet the
mountains cause air to rise
and to cool enough to
form cloud and rain.

❒ (below) Air flowing from the Pacific Ocean up the
windward side of the central mountains of Hawaii.
Notice the coastal area by the airport is cloud free.

By plotting chart after chart as each new set of reports came in, the forecaster was able to see how the air was changing and so make a forecast for a few hours or even a day ahead.

Forecasting is not, however, just a matter of observing cloud patterns on maps. It relies on understanding how the atmosphere works, how the air moves and what causes rain. Sometimes the ways of obtaining this understanding can be dramatic. For example, in the 1910s planes were used to fly into clouds to discover how they worked. From such studies forecasters came to understand how a depression worked, and from this they could interpret their maps even more effectively.

> Weather forecasters use information from satellites and some of the world's fastest computers to make sure that forecasts are accurate for a few hours ahead.

Weather forecasting still relies on reports from widely scattered stations. For example, the hurricane-force winds that caused widespread damage to England in 1987 were missed by forecasters because a crucial weather ship had been taken off its ocean station. Without the information from the weather ship, the forecasters were 'blind' and could not warn people to be prepared. The United States National Hurricane Service would be similarly blind without its network of weather stations on the Caribbean islands and in the ocean.

Forecasting around the world

Because so much of what we do depends on the weather, weather forecasting is important in almost every country. To allow the weather to be forecast accurately, countries now share their weather records. High-speed supercomputers help plot charts quickly and accurately.

But although worldwide charts give valuable information, people also want to know what is happening in their own local area. To help with this, sophisticated electronic devices are used.

For example, satellites can give 'snapshot' images of the clouds as they view the Earth from high orbits. These are the images you see on the television reports. Radar can be used to pinpoint where rain is falling and how heavy it is. It can even help determine where tornadoes might be forming.

These reports help forecasters give very accurate forecasts for a few hours ahead and, just as importantly, allow viewers to see the patterns for themselves and thus to understand better what is likely to happen in their own local area.

❐ (below) Australia is a huge country, but its weather patterns are relatively simple, consisting of low pressure regions that move from west to east. Severe winds occur when one of the low pressure regions is squashed against strong high pressure regions as shown in the map on page 9.

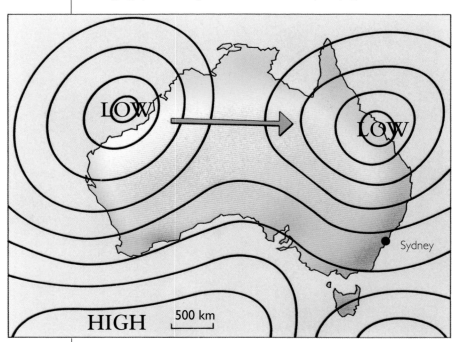

Forecasting in the United States

The continental United States is one of the world's largest countries, stretching from subtropics to the edges of cold regions. The north and east also experience depressions that quickly track from west to east.

A weather forecast for the whole country can only be given in very general terms. For example, the movement of weather fronts is most used for the weather of the northern states, while for the central regions it is more important to know about the chances of thunderstorms and tornadoes. Weather forecasters also have to take account of the effect of the great ranges of mountains that lie across the country – the Rockies and the Appalachians, each of which often have their own weather.

To make some sense of all this variation, local forecasts are a vital addition to national reports.

So that they can talk about the many types of rainfall in the same terms, forecasters in the United States emphasise the chances of rain, rather than the features of the atmosphere that might cause it. Thus they report, for example, a "30% chance of a shower in the afternoon".

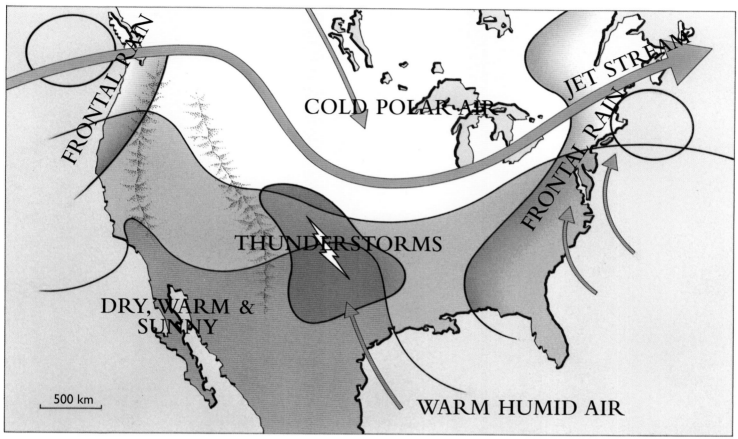

Forecasting in the United Kingdom

The United Kingdom is much smaller than the other countries shown on these pages, but because it is situated where warm air from the tropics meets cold air from the arctic, its weather is more variable than almost anywhere else on Earth. The weather in one place may be quite different from a place just 100 km away. As a result forecasters have to concentrate on what will happen in local areas just a few hours ahead.

Newspaper weather forecasts are only of general interest to such a variable scene, and many people now update themselves with regular television bulletins.

One key piece of technical assistance used widely for local forecasting is weather radar, especially because it can show the actual pattern of rain as it moves across the country. Radar, together with detailed satellite pictures, allow forecasters to pick out weather fronts and see more clearly how changes are progressing.

Most weather forecasting concentrates on the passage of fronts, which tend to track right across the country every few days. Only occasionally do regions of high pressure bring settled, easily forecast weather.

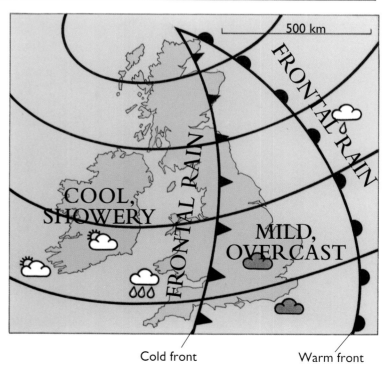

Cold front   Warm front

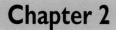
Weather hazards and disasters

Even the world's fastest computers and information from satellites can do little other than to prepare people for unusual or extreme weather events. The weather can pose dangers for many reasons. Hazardous conditions can be caused by excess rain, snow, fog, high or low temperatures, strong winds and droughts.

Disasters happen because people are not prepared for these severe weather events or because they do not take the right action when severe weather threatens.

For the most part we live comfortably with the weather. But from time to time the pattern of the weather takes on an unusual form. The wind may get unusually strong, temperatures might soar or plummet, rain may be extremely heavy or may not come when expected, snow may fall or fog banks blanket the land.

If these conditions are outside the 'normal' range of the weather, they are called extreme events. Everyone should plan for extreme events, and most good building designs and city plans allow for all but the most the violent events.

❒ (left) Ships wrecked along a storm-racked coast after the 1894 hurricane which passed over Calcutta, India.

Weather poses most hazards to those people do not live in properly designed buildings, or who live in places most prone to extreme events. For example in the world's shanty towns and near the coast in the track of tropical cyclones (hurricanes and typhoons), both property and lives may be put in danger.

If many people are killed or injured or much property is destroyed by extreme weather we call this a disaster.

> Unusual weather events – called extremes – cause the greatest risk to life and property because they are rare and people are often not trained or equipped to deal with them.

Common weather hazards are:

☞ high temperatures, which may cause heatstroke;

☞ low temperatures, which may cause frostbite or a dangerous cooling of the body called hypothermia;

☞ low rainfall, which may bring on drought, causing people and animals to die of thirst, or, more likely, killing crops and causing famine;

☞ high rainfall, which may cause flooding, destroy crops, put lives at risk and damage buildings;

☞ high winds, which may destroy buildings and harm the people inside, or cause tidal waves that flood coastal regions;

☞ fog, which makes it difficult to see and can lead to traffic accidents;

☞ blizzards, which cause drifting snow that may bury animals in fields and cause people to be stranded in their vehicles

☞ calm conditions, which can increase pollution in cities and may cause or worsen breathing problems.

Severe winds

Tropical cyclones are spiralling masses of air where the winds rise to over 120 km/hr. They are called hurricanes in the Atlantic and eastern Pacific (from the West Indian word *hurrican*, meaning big wind) and typhoons (from the Chinese *taifun* which means great wind) in the western Pacific.

Tropical cyclones form only when moisture evaporates from oceans with temperatures above 27°C. The oceans transfer heat directly to the lowest levels of the air, causing the air to rise. At the same time, enormous amounts of water are taken up by the air as water vapour, or moisture.

As the air rises, it cools and cannot hold all of the moisture. The moisture thus starts to turn back into water droplets, at the same time releasing heat energy which causes the air to rise faster still. If these conditions affect air that is far enough away from the Equator, the spin of the Earth will cause the rising air to spin as well. This mass of fast-spinning, cloud-filled air is called a tropical cyclone. Cyclones only die away when they pass over cold ocean water or lands, as the supply of hot moist air is then cut off.

Once a cyclone has formed it behaves like a spinning top, whirling around and around and at the same time following a wobbly path across the ocean that is steered by the prevailing winds.

The power generated by a single tropical cyclone is immense. Each day a cyclone may contain the same energy as a country uses in power for the whole year. Not surprisingly, such concentrated energy has mighty effects on buildings and other structures.

❐ (above) A hurricane seen from a satellite. Notice how the shape is picked out by the spiralling walls of cloud that rise up to 12 km into the sky.

The centre of the tropical storm is a cloud-free eye, perhaps no more than a few tens of kilometres across, the only part of the storm where air is actually sinking. The winds swirling around the eye have speeds up to 300 km/hr.

Tornado

A tornado (from the Spanish *tronada*, or thunderstorm) is also known as a twister. Tornadoes are tightly spinning, funnel-shaped clouds that appear to hang from the bottom of a thundercloud.

The winds in the centre of the funnel may exceed 800 km/hr but they stretch over a very small area of just a few tens of metres. They quickly pass over the ground, but the destruction they can cause in just a few minutes' passage can be tremendous.

Many people experience cold blustery winds as a thunderstorm passes by. A tornado is probably an extreme version of this wind that develops a tight, swirling motion.

Tornadoes are not cyclones, but because tropical cyclones have great walls of thunderclouds inside them, tornadoes often occur *inside* them.

Tornadoes are produced as air is sucked very quickly into the bases of individual thunderstorms. They can form over land or over water, where they are called waterspouts.

Inside a tornado the air is very thin (it is an area of very low pressure). Many buildings that have been tightly shuttered for protection often explode as a tornado passes because the air pressure inside the building is much greater than that outside.

Tornadoes are experienced widely, from the cool lands of the UK to the warmer areas of Australia, but they are by far the most common in the United States, which holds the world record at an average of 1000 each year.

☐ (above) Hurricane-force winds sometimes occur in the mid-latitudes. The ship shown above was driven aground when such winds affected the south of England in October 1987.

The effects of tropical cyclones

Tropical cyclones can destroy property and kill people. Strong winds may blow down buildings and trees, but nine-tenths of all people killed by such storms drown. Tropical cyclones actually draw water towards them, so that the level of the sea (the level of the tide) may increase by up to 10 m. This causes a tidal wave to surge onto shore, claiming the most lives.

☐ (right) When a tidal wave surges over low-lying areas, such as the barrier islands fringing the eastern and southern United States coasts, almost nothing survives.

☐ (above) The funnel that forms at the base of a thundercloud can suck up houses and trains. Fortunately the destruction of any one tornado rarely lasts more than a few minutes.

Mid-latitude storms

Extremely fierce winds are not as common in mid-latitudes as near the tropics, but occasionally depressions become very intense and lead to hurricane-force winds. They can be particularly disastrous because buildings are often not designed for such very rare winds.

One such disaster happened in October 1987, when a depression tracked across northern France and southern England. It reached northern France at 1 a.m. and southern England at 4 a.m. By late morning it had gone, but it had left a £1 billion trail of havoc. Huge ships caught at sea had been blown onto the shore; other, less fortunate ships were sunk. Roofs were torn from buildings, trees were uprooted by the million and vehicles tossed about in the streets like playthings. It was made worse by the fact that few buildings had been designed to withstand such winds.

Extreme events

We all expect the weather to vary a little from day to day, but sometimes the weather varies greatly from normal. Extreme events are the occasions when weather records are broken.

Extreme weather events cause disasters because many people are not prepared. They are especially at risk if they live beside rivers or at the coast.

Among record temperature extremes, the highest temperature ever recorded is 58°C in the Libyan desert, and the lowest is -89°C in Antarctica. The most rainfall in one day, 1870 mm (nearly 2 m), happened on La Reunion island in the Indian Ocean. Cherrapungi, in India, holds the world's monthly maximum at 9299 mm (just over 9 m) and for the year, 26,461mm (over 26 m).

The greatest yearly snowfall recorded was on Mt Rainier, USA, at 31 m. The wind record is 371 km/hr, which was recorded on Mt Washington in the United States. The greatest temperature change during a 24-hour period in the United States occurred in Montana, when the temperature fell 56.5 degrees, from 7.8°C to -48.3°C.

Sudden disasters

The effect of extremes of weather can often produce horrific disasters. Perhaps the worst recorded event of a direct weather event was .the storm that drowned one million people who lived on the Ganges delta in Bangladesh in 1970. Weather conditions can also cause floods indirectly, for example, by unusually wet weather. This is what caused the Hwang He river in China to flood in 1887, killing perhaps 900,000 people.

Strong winds tend to occur in small areas, creating a trail of destruction. Hurricane-force winds are produced by tropical storms, but the fiercest winds of all – in tornadoes – are

Severe rain and floods

Flooding is not always a result of heavy rain. For example, strong winds can blow sea water onto shore until it floods low-lying coastal lands. If a high tide coincides with a strong onshore wind, the results can be disastrous.

This kind of flooding happened in 1953 when strong winds blowing across the North Sea occurred at the same time as one of the year's highest tides. The result was thousands of deaths from drowning in United Kingdom, The Netherlands and Belgium.

Coastal flooding has become far worse in the developing world as more and more people are forced to live on flood-prone land that had traditionally been avoided. The catalogue of disasters in countries like Bangladesh makes horrific reading. Every few years, Bangladesh can expect to experience a major flooding disaster that will kill over a quarter of a million people.

River floods are not as disastrous as coastal floods. They can be very local such as when a torrential thunderstorm

breaks over a small rocky river basin. In deserts, where there are no soils to soak up the moisture, such rain causes flash floods. However, because deserts are home to few people, the loss of life from flash floods is small.

Springtime floods occur when snow melts in mountain regions. A sudden burst of warm air may cause very rapid melting and cause the rivers to flood. In this case, although the flooding is inconvenient and may cause damage, few lives are lost. Because this kind of flooding occurs quite often, people are prepared for its effects.

Flooding is much more serious when unusually heavy and prolonged rain falls over a large part of a major river basin. There comes a stage when the rain can no longer be soaked up by the soil and it begins to run over the surface, causing rivers to burst their banks. The most important recent event of this kind affected the Mississippi basin in the United States in 1993.

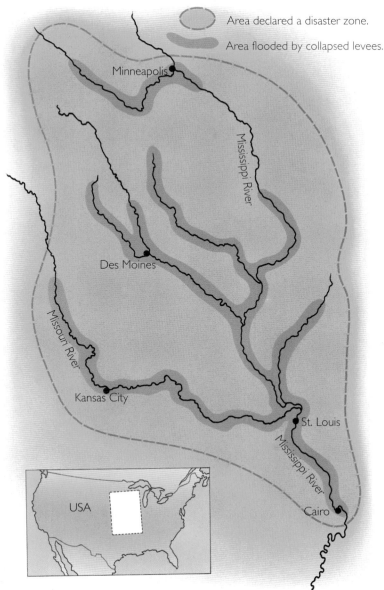

Area declared a disaster zone.

Area flooded by collapsed levees.

❏ (above) This map shows the extent of the flooding in the "Great Flood" of 1993. The first flooding began in mid-June when the soils of the headwaters of the Mississippi, still saturated with water from the spring snowmelt, were not able to soak up water from torrential summer rainstorms.

Once the flooding began, the flood wave moved slowly down the river, taking a month to reach the area near to Cairo, Illinois. The amount of water was so great that it reached 15.1 m at St. Louis, where it nearly overtopped the levees that had been built up to 15.9 m. Many other places were not as fortunate, and the levees collapsed under the enormous pressure of the water.

❏ (left and right) When heavy rain causes rivers to burst their banks, the result can be catastrophic. Much of the damage is done by the sediment carried by the water as much as by the water itself. These pictures was taken near Vancouver, Canada.

produced by thunderstorms. In 1925, a tornado moving through the south-central United States caused widespread damage and killed nearly 700 people.

Prolonged disasters

Storms may leave a trail of destruction, but they do not last very long. On the other hand, some extreme weather can last for many years.

Disasters are most severe in places where many people live together in exposed places. The poor usually suffer most, because they often live in poorly built homes in the least safe places.

There is almost no way of escaping the effects of such long-term change, and tens or even hundreds of millions of people can be affected.

Drought – a lack of water for a long period of time – is the biggest cause of long-term disaster. It can cause not just a shortage of water to drink, but also loss of crops, thus turning disaster into famine.

Areas prone to unpredictable and long-term drought lie mainly between 15 and 20 degrees north and south of the Equator. These are areas that have a near-desert climate. Droughts in such regions occur when rain-bearing westerly winds take an unusual path. Such places include West Africa (the Sahel), South Africa, Brazil, Australia and India.

Drought is most harmful in those parts of the world where there are large numbers of people whose survival depends on getting a good harvest every year. For example, from 1968 to 1974 and again in the mid 1980s, the rains failed year after year in the Sahel. The droughts caused hundreds of thousands of people and millions of animals to die from starvation when the crops failed and the grazing lands did not produce enough grass.

El Niño: a global weather disaster

Many extreme weather events do not affect very large areas. But recently scientists have learned that some of the world's disasters are linked to a change in the whole of the world's weather patterns. They have also discovered that worldwide disasters can occur more regularly than was once thought. The period of disasters that has received most attention is known as El Niño, and its effects occur once every four to six years.

The sequence of changes begin over the warm waters of the South Pacific. During El Niño, the atmosphere becomes disturbed and the winds reverse. This pushes water eastward across the Pacific to pile up against the Americas. This surge of water may take two months to subside, and eventually the warm water reaches America, pushing aside the cold ocean currents that normally well up at the shores. Winds blowing over these warm waters create the balmy breeze called El Niño.

When conditions in the tropics change, there is a worldwide effect. In 1982, for example, the effect of El Niño was particularly strong, bringing extreme weather to many areas. It caused drought, bush fire and famine in places as widely scattered as India, Australia and South Africa by cutting off the vital monsoon rains. It brought typhoons to Tahiti and floods and landslides to Ecuador. Flooding in the streets of shanty towns then caused health epidemics.

El Niño changes caused fish breeding grounds to move. Fishermen in South America went bankrupt, sea bird flocks died as their food supply was cut off. In the same areas, 'freak' storms racked the coasts and many lost their homes and livelihoods.

It also caused the coldest weather and highest heating bills for decades to the eastern seaboard of the United States and sent temperatures in Europe plummeting. In Birmingham, it fell to -28°C, making the city colder than Siberia, and the sea began to freeze off the coast of East Anglia.

❐ (above) In the developing world, droughts cause rivers to run dry and force people to go to amazing lengths to find water. Animals suffer badly, and millions die.

❏ (below) This map shows the widespread effects that can be produced by the global weather disaster called El Niño.

Warm water moves eastward

Floods and storms

Drought

Warm water moves eastwa

Drought

Drought

Drought

❏ (above and below) When excessive drought occurs, natural vegetation can dry out so much that the smallest spark can cause damaging fires. Lightning is often the cause of many such fires.

California, USA, and Sydney, Australia, have suffered particularly in El Niño droughts, with bush fires destroying many of the wooded suburbs. These pictures shows the destruction and how people try to rebuild.

Hazards of ignorance

Many tragedies happen simply because people have been 'caught out' by the weather. For example, those who go walking in mountains sometimes die because normal weather is more severe than they have prepared for. Mountains can be clear one minute and covered in freezing fog the next. Without proper protection, this change can kill.

> People can face disaster when they find themselves in areas where they are unfamiliar with the weather.

But disasters affecting millions can also be caused by normal patterns of weather. This happens most commonly to immigrants who have little long-term knowledge of the weather in the area they have just arrived in.

Perhaps the most famous example of this is the region east of the Rocky Mountains in the United States which became known as the Dust Bowl. Here, unfamiliarity with the climate caused much of the land to be farmed improperly. The Dust Bowl lands have a natural cycle of wet years followed by dry years. Immigrants arrived during the wet years. When the drier years followed, crops failed and left the soil exposed. Many millions of tonnes of soil were simply blown away from the fields and many farmers were made bankrupt.

Modern hazards

One of the main weather-related hazards brought about by modern living is air pollution. It occurs especially under high pressure, anticyclonic conditions. At such times, the air is sinking and conditions are calm, with only gentle breezes. This can allow local effects to become severe.

One of the greatest problems affects cities that lie in basins. Here the effects of exhausts gases and particles released by traffic can

Fog

Sometimes clouds can gather at ground level. When the visibility is less than 100 m, people speak of fog; between 100 and 200 m, they speak of mist.

Fog may occur inland, especially in autumn and winter, when the ground cools, and the air is still moist. Fog may also occur by the sea when moist air moves over cold ocean currents.

Fog is a hazard because it is difficult to see through it. It is a particular hazard to fast-moving means of transport such as aircraft and road vehicles. Fog is also unpredictable. A driver may be in brilliant sunshine one moment and in a dense fog bank the next.

❒ (left) Mist is visibility between 100 and 200 m.

❏ (above) The famous fog of San Francisco and other parts of the Californian coast is produced by heating inland. This pulls in air from off the shore, causing it to flow over the cold Californian coastal ocean current. Here it is cooled, producing shallow, but very persistent fog banks.

❏ (below) Fog forming over the cold waters of this Canadian mountain river. On land it is warmer and no fog occurs.

❏ (above and right) The variable nature of fog can best be seen when it is just forming or as it clears away. These three pictures were taken within a period of five minutes, and during this short time the fog both thickened and then dispersed.

The fog has been caused by warm air being pulled over cold sea water, and the fog is very thin. The air above the cliff top is clear and clouds can be seen.

produce a killing mixture called smog (see opposite). Normally, winds would carry the worst of the pollution away (and thus sharing the hazard with the surrounding countryside!), but under calm conditions the pollutants simply build up near the ground. Toxic gases include ozone and carbon monoxide.

Modern automobiles are equipped with filters called CATALYTIC CONVERTERS in their exhausts. These attempt to cut down on pollution, but they are only used in wealthy industrial countries.

Forecasting severe weather events

One of the most vital tasks of the forecaster is to give people notice of weather conditions that may threaten property or life. Such extreme, or severe, weather events include blizzards, hurricanes, tornadoes, and heavy rainfall that can lead to flooding and fog.

> Many severe weather events are difficult to forecast because they are rare and because they develop so quickly.

In some countries where severe events are common, special government centres try to forecast possible hazards. One of these is the United States National Hurricane Centre in Coral Gables, Florida. It tracks hurricanes in the Atlantic, Caribbean, and eastern Pacific Oceans.

Forecasting has been made all the more urgent by the fact that some areas with high populations may need more than a day to organise evacuation. Unfortunately, accurate forecasts for extreme events like hurricanes, typhoons and tornadoes still cannot be made more than a few hours ahead. And forecasts are of little help to the poor people of developing countries who have no means of escape anyway.

Smog

Smog is a combination of smoke and fog. It first became serious as populations concentrated into cities during the INDUSTRIAL REVOLUTION. At first it was caused almost entirely by burning coal.

During times of high pressure, smoke particles were carried from chimneys into the air, but they were trapped by an invisible warm layer of air above. In basins and valleys, the air becomes particularly concentrated, and levels of smoke may build up to be so great that they cause people severe breathing problems. Those with asthma and other breathing complaints are particularly at risk.

One of the worst occurrences of traditional smog occurred in London during 1952. A large anticyclone settled over the London basin, trapping the air below. There weather was very cold, encouraging people to burn more coal. As a result the amount of smoke in the air grew to alarming proportions. It is believed that over 4000 people died as a direct result of the smog.

The health hazard of coal smog became so obvious that many governments worldwide brought in laws that restricted the use of smoky fuels. But in any case the use of coal was declining as new central heating systems used oil and natural gas.

Unfortunately, the smog problem continues, because as coal declined, the use of oil in vehicles increased, so that now the pollution is caused primarily by road users. This is a different kind of smog than that made by coal. It causes breathing problems in the winter but it is actually far more severe in the summer. This is because the gases released by exhausts change chemically in the presence of strong sunlight. This type of smog – called photochemical smog – particularly affects hot locations such as Mexico City and Los Angeles.

 (right) This is a picture of Los Angeles taken from near the airport. The pollution has reduced visibility drastically.

❐ (below) These pictures show the contrast in the air pollution over Mexico City between a time when the air is calm and when there is a breeze. Because of the increase in traffic in this, the world's biggest city, it now takes stronger winds to blow away the pollution than in the past. Even for people without health problems, the level of pollution on a calm winter day causes the sore throats and stinging eyes.

❐ (left) Air pollution is more common in basins and valleys than in any other type of landscape. This is because the air can become trapped during periods of high pressure.

This picture shows clearly the rising smoke being held near the ground by an invisible 'lid' in the atmosphere.

Chapter 3

Climate, the past and the future

One of the most important questions that scientists are seeking to answer is whether or not the world's climate will change. The answer to this question is vital, because changes affect so many of the things on which our lives depend. At present there is still not enough clear evidence that people are causing the climate to change, but the evidence is mounting.

Many people take the climate for granted. They assume that the pattern of weather in one year will be much like the next. So many things we do depend on things staying much the same. Engineers plan for the reservoirs we need by assuming the climate will not change; farmers plan the crops they will grow and harvest; clothes shops even depend on the climate remaining the same to make sure they have suitable goods in stock.

But are we right to think that the climate does stay the same? What would we do if it changed quickly? And more importantly, are we doing anything that might cause change or speed it up?

These are some of the questions that scientists all over the world are asking, because the answers are so vital to our future.

❏ (left) The world's climate has always changed, but now people may be causing changes to happen faster than ever before. Much of the cause is thought to be the way we burn fossil fuels to power our world.

Climate clues from the past

During the vast amount of time since the Earth formed, the climates of the world have changed enormously. Some changes have been brought about by changing positions of the continents, such as new mountains forming and then being eroded away, others by alterations to the air itself.

The story in the world's rocks shows the climate continually changing. For example, a bed of coal seen in a cliff tells that the region was, at one time, warm and humid, like the tropical swamps today. Other rocks, above and below it may show that the same land was once desert, or that it once was covered in ice.

The Earth's climate today

The present period in the Earth's great history is unusual, because the Earth has only been colder than it is today for five per cent of its history.

At the moment, there is a larger difference in temperature between the icy poles and the Equator than has been normal in the past. This contrast pulls warm air and warm ocean waters from the tropics to the poles and sends cold air and cold water back by return. But for most of the Earth's history the poles have not been covered with ice and the flows of air and water over the Earth have been much less marked. This means that in the past the weather over the world was much less variable and the atmosphere probably moved in quite different patterns.

The Earth shows many natural signs of change, both long term and over just a few years.

We are probably in a temporary warm period between two parts of a long Ice Age that started two million years ago. Since the Ice Age began, there have been as many as twenty advances of the ice with ice sheets moving south as far as London and New York.

Climate changes that could have affected history

Can climate have affected the way that people behaved in the past?

It was a major change in the world's climate that created the Ice Age. During much of this time water was locked up on land and the sea level fell. This created land bridges that allowed people to move from one continent to another. It is most likely that the Americas, for example, were first colonised by humans at this time.

All societies depend on farming for their survival. This means that societies are also affected by changes in climate. An ancient civilisation of northwestern India grew up and flourished about 6000 years ago at a time of plentiful rainfall, but died out about 2200 years later when the climate changed and there were centuries of drought. A change in the climate and a long period of drought may also have caused the Anasazi Indians to disappear from southwestern North America around the year 1300.

A period of warmth may have allowed ancient Britons to cultivate the soils of hills and mountains. But a change to colder conditions about 600 years ago may have made farming in these areas impossible, forcing the farmers of this time to abandon their land.

❏ (below) A few stones surrounding a well are all that remain of this Australian settlement. It had to be abandoned because of drought.

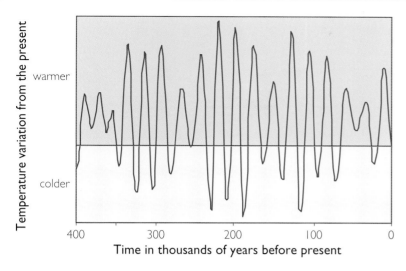

(left) In the last half a million years the average temperature of the Earth has gone up and down more or less regularly. This diagram shows that it has, on average, been warmer in the past than it is now.
The changes shown were climatic changes, each occurring over centuries. But these great natural changes in climate make it so hard to decide whether the effects of people have caused any long-term warming or cooling.

(below) Differences in the thickness of tree rings show that there have been warmer or wetter periods as well as drier and colder ones in the last few centuries. Many of these changes occur in cycles. Bristlecone Pine trees give a 5000-year record.

Changes in the weather are not always changes in the climate

Changes in the climate are long-term changes. Here are two famous examples where changes in the weather for just a few years caused a dramatic change in history.

The great migration of people from Ireland to America was in part due to the poor harvests brought on by just a few years of unfavourable summers. A few years later the summers were favourable again.

Even conditions for the French Revolution could have been in part influenced by variations in weather from year to year. In 1787 the rainfall was very high and the following spring there was a heat wave which caused the crops to fail. In 1789 wheat reached record prices, many of which could not be afforded by the people. The French Revolution started with the storming of the Bastille in 1789.

But the change to colder, wetter conditions that affected Europe in the 17th century was a real change in climate and lasted for about a century.

(below) Changes in the climate are often signalled by advances and retreat of glaciers. The 'Little Ice Age' that caused the freezing of European rivers in the 17th century was matched by advances in glaciers; at present the glaciers are retreating, perhaps signalling a warmer phase.

During this time the temperature has changed from much colder than today to much warmer. Even in quite recent times it has changed: between about 900 and 1150 it was much warmer than today, while between 1550 and 1850 it was cold enough to be called the Little Ice Age. Many paintings (such as those of the Dutch artist Breughel) show scenes of ice and snow that simply do not occur today.

People v Earth – who is in control of the climate?

Since the earliest days of the Earth, the Sun has gradually become stronger, and it now gives out about a third more energy than it did 2 billion years ago. But throughout this time the temperature of the atmosphere has, on average, remained the same. So is there a way in which the Earth itself is able to control its own temperature and, thus, the world's climates?

> The Earth may be able to control its own climate to some extent, showing how living things are vital in ways that were previously not understood.

As the Sun has become stronger, more tiny floating sea creatures called plankton have thrived. As they die and their bodies sink to the ocean floor and do not decompose, they lock up the carbon as rock. In this way the carbon dioxide of the air has been reduced over the last two billion years, balancing out the affect of the greater heating power of the Sun.

Now some scientists have begun to worry about the way in which, by burning coal, oil and gas, we are pumping back within a few years the carbon dioxide that was removed over millions of years. They worry that the extra carbon dioxide will allow the Earth's atmosphere to warm up again at a rate that growing plankton cannot balance, and that this will have a great effect on the climates all over the globe.

Are we altering the world's climate?

We now know that the atmosphere changes quite often, and that because the key features of change – carbon dioxide and water vapour – can be so easily changed by human action, we may be able to change our own climate. The trouble is we do not yet know how. Here are some of the main thoughts being raised at the moment.

❐ (right) Measurements of temperature suggest that the Earth is warming. Most people assume that this is because of the amount of fossil fuels we burn and the amount of forest we have cut down and replaced with farmland. This is a very difficult thing to judge, however, because many other factors are involved and the changes are not yet very large. But if it is true, the temperature of the Earth may well reach the levels shown in the diagram. The suggested rise is about 2°C in the next century. This may not seem much, but it only took a lowering of temperature of 5°C to cause the recent Ice Age!

☛ **Planting more trees takes carbon dioxide out of the air**
Countries in the northern hemisphere have recently planted far more trees than they have cut down, so the growing trees may use up some of the extra carbon dioxide.

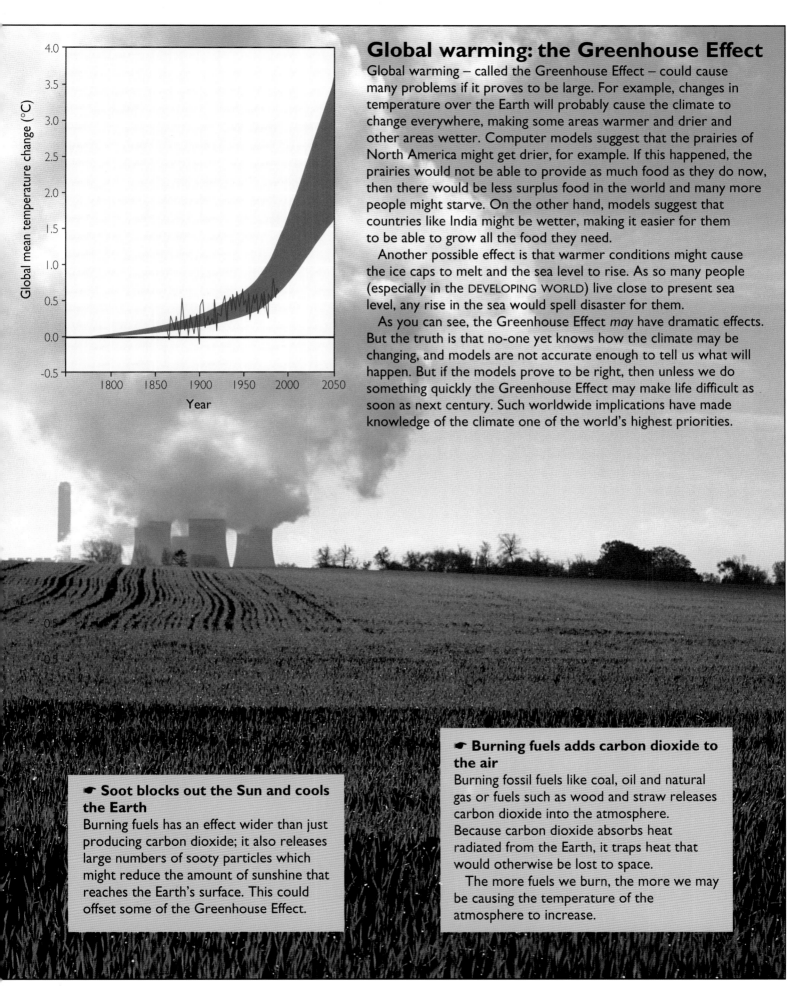

Global warming: the Greenhouse Effect

Global warming – called the Greenhouse Effect – could cause many problems if it proves to be large. For example, changes in temperature over the Earth will probably cause the climate to change everywhere, making some areas warmer and drier and other areas wetter. Computer models suggest that the prairies of North America might get drier, for example. If this happened, the prairies would not be able to provide as much food as they do now, then there would be less surplus food in the world and many more people might starve. On the other hand, models suggest that countries like India might be wetter, making it easier for them to be able to grow all the food they need.

Another possible effect is that warmer conditions might cause the ice caps to melt and the sea level to rise. As so many people (especially in the DEVELOPING WORLD) live close to present sea level, any rise in the sea would spell disaster for them.

As you can see, the Greenhouse Effect *may* have dramatic effects. But the truth is that no-one yet knows how the climate may be changing, and models are not accurate enough to tell us what will happen. But if the models prove to be right, then unless we do something quickly the Greenhouse Effect may make life difficult as soon as next century. Such worldwide implications have made knowledge of the climate one of the world's highest priorities.

☛ Soot blocks out the Sun and cools the Earth

Burning fuels has an effect wider than just producing carbon dioxide; it also releases large numbers of sooty particles which might reduce the amount of sunshine that reaches the Earth's surface. This could offset some of the Greenhouse Effect.

☛ Burning fuels adds carbon dioxide to the air

Burning fossil fuels like coal, oil and natural gas or fuels such as wood and straw releases carbon dioxide into the atmosphere. Because carbon dioxide absorbs heat radiated from the Earth, it traps heat that would otherwise be lost to space.

The more fuels we burn, the more we may be causing the temperature of the atmosphere to increase.

World climates

Climate

- Tropical rainforest
- Savanna
- Desert and semi-arid
- Warm temperate
- Cool temperate
- Mediterranean
- Steppe and prairie
- Mountain
- Cold

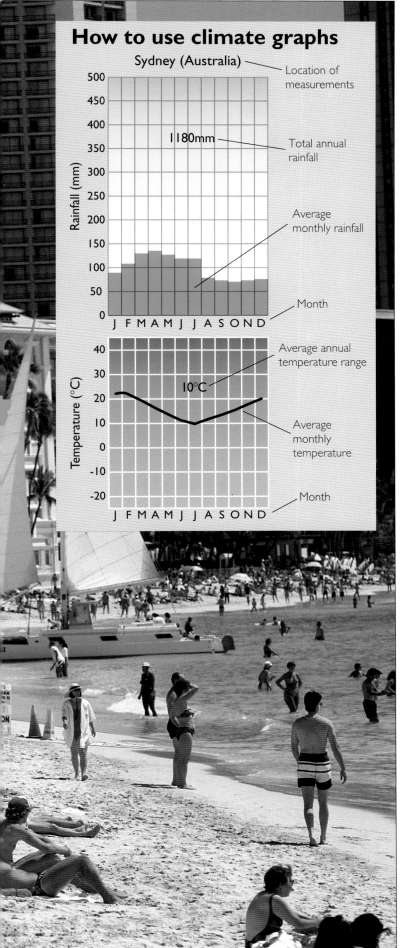

How to use climate graphs

Sydney (Australia) — Location of measurements

1180mm — Total annual rainfall

Average monthly rainfall

Month

Average annual temperature range

10°C

Average monthly temperature

Month

Chapter 5

A guide to the world's climates

The world's climates affect how the world works and many of the things that people do. For example, climate influences the way the world's landscapes form, which plants grow in the landscape, where and when people go on holiday, and what kind of designs are best for people's homes.

Climate is such an important way of understanding the world that its words are bound up in many expressions for other things (for example, *desert* landscapes, *tropical* rainforest.)

The humid tropics

The humid tropics occupy the zone to either side of the Equator. They all receive large amounts of rain, although while some areas receive rain throughout the year, others receive rain only in one period.

Because the temperature remains high throughout the year, there is no summer or winter, but rather a dry season and a wet season.

❏ (left) The most commonly used climatic classification was developed by Wladimir Köppen early in this century. He reasoned that because the pattern of climate influences which plants can succeed, a world map showing patterns of natural vegetation will have many similarities to a world map showing climates.

Köppen searched through easily obtained values of rainfall and temperature for recording stations all over the world and found values that matched the boundaries of major vegetation types. He found nine major categories, which are shown on the map on the opposite page.

In some areas that have rainfall throughout the year, there are simply no seasons at all. In fact, in most of these areas the changes that occur between the heat of day and the cool of night are far greater than the difference between the hottest and coolest times of the year

In a zone that lies within five degrees of the Equator, many coastal areas receive rain more or less every day throughout the year. In these areas there is a daily cycle of weather, with sunny mornings followed by rain in the early afternoon.

In the tropics the Sun is overhead throughout the year and temperatures remain high. Tropical regions therefore do not have winter and summer.

Instead there is a great difference between rainy seasons and dry seasons. Thus people use the words wet season and dry season.

The world's biggest forests (the Amazon and the Congo) also release enough moisture from their leaves to act just like oceans, providing the moisture for rainfall every day, even in areas thousands of kilometres from the oceans.

In this part of the world, the climate greatly depends on the forests. Without them, these areas would be far drier. This is one reason that many people believe that the tropical rainforests should not be cut down.

Away from the Equator, rain tends to fall for just part of the year – the wet season. The wet season coincides with the time of year when the Sun is most overhead, so the rainy season in the Northern Hemisphere tends to be from May to October, and in the Southern Hemisphere between November and April.

Tropical rainforest climate

Examples: Borneo, Cameroun, Rondonia state of Brazil, South Malaysia, Singapore, Papua New Guinea, tropical Pacific islands.

All months have average temperatures above 18 °C and a range through the year of less than 6 °C. The main variations are from the daily cycle of the weather.

Many of the regions that lie astride the Equator have weather that is very similar all year round. Areas within five degrees of the Equator vary, on average, by no more than a few degrees Celsius from the hottest to the coldest months. Many, although not all, equatorial areas also have rainfall throughout the year and so do not experience wet or dry seasons.

These warm humid conditions have allowed the most extraordinary forests to grow in a girdle about the Earth. They are called tropical rainforests.

Tropical islands are surrounded by ocean, so it is easy to see the source of the moisture that forms the clouds that give the torrential rainstorms on most days. But parts of the world's biggest rainforests, such as in the Amazon Basin, are thousands of kilometres from the ocean and there are no constant winds to drive the moisture ashore. Instead the moisture is provided by the trees themselves. Their roots pump rainfall from the soil up through the trunks and out through the leaves.

By this process, called transpiration, plants gather the nourishment they need for life, but they also give vast amounts of moisture back to the air, allowing the clouds to form and more rain to fall.

(right) Manaus (Location: 3°S;60°W) is a Brazilian city 1000 km from the ocean. It has no dry season, although there is less rain from June to September. The rain that falls in this period is almost all due to the forests releasing moisture to the air.

Notice that the temperature hardly changes throughout the year.

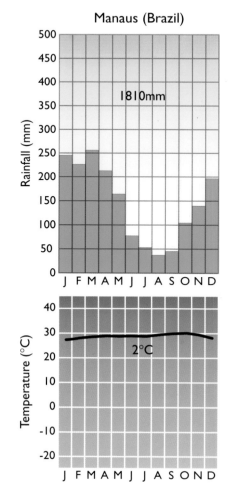

Manaus (Brazil)

1810mm

2°C

Singapore

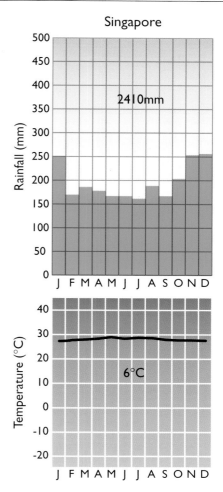

❐ (above) Singapore (Location: 1°N;104°E) has a tropical rainforest climate. The coast experiences onshore breezes that make the hot humid conditions much easier to bear than inland.

❐ (below) Rice flourishes in the rainforest climate of Bali.

❐ (above) Traditional building for the humid tropics. Because there are no prevailing winds, the only places where cooling breezes occur are along the coast. Elsewhere it is always 'sticky and sultry'. Most traditional buildings are designed to keep forest animals at bay. Otherwise they need to be as airy as possible, for example, with walls made simply of loosely tied bamboo.

❐ (left) Daily thunderstorms are one of the features of a rainforest climate like that of the Cook Islands.

Monsoon

Monsoon comes from an Arabic word meaning 'season'. It is a term used to describe climates that affect hot areas with a season of torrential rainfall which often begins abruptly. Monsoons are a climatic variation on the more normal pattern of wet and dry seasons that occurs throughout much of the tropics.

Sudden changes between seasons are not common, and where they occur they reflect special local conditions. For this reason it is not possible to explain all monsoon areas in the same way. In West Africa, for example, the monsoon occurs when dry, scorching Trade Winds from the Sahara Desert are suddenly replaced with moist winds from the Atlantic Ocean.

In India, the start of the rainy season occurs when air from the oceans is drawn over the fiercely hot continent in June. But the abrupt start of the monsoon is caused by the special way air moves across the Himalayas.

> In most parts of the tropics it is hot throughout the year, and the words 'summer' and 'winter' have no meaning. Instead, the seasons are marked by rainfall, and people speak of the wet season and the dry season.

The end of the wet season is always less abrupt than the start. It occurs gradually, about three months after the start of the monsoon, as the Sun shines less fiercely and the continent cools down and stops drawing air from the oceans.

Dry climates

Large parts of the world experience a climate where the amount of rain that falls is small and very unreliable. The world's greatest deserts lie in a belt on both sides of the tropics of Capricorn and Cancer. The North African

The seasons of the tropics

The tropics experience seasons because of the movement of the overhead Sun. Because the Sun is always high in the sky, all places are hot; seasons are created by rain.

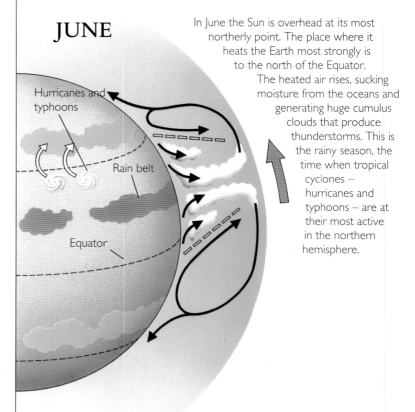

JUNE

Hurricanes and typhoons

Rain belt

Equator

In June the Sun is overhead at its most northerly point. The place where it heats the Earth most strongly is to the north of the Equator. The heated air rises, sucking moisture from the oceans and generating huge cumulus clouds that produce thunderstorms. This is the rainy season, the time when tropical cyclones – hurricanes and typhoons – are at their most active in the northern hemisphere.

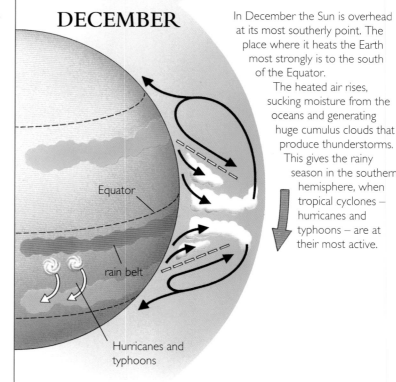

DECEMBER

Equator

rain belt

Hurricanes and typhoons

In December the Sun is overhead at its most southerly point. The place where it heats the Earth most strongly is to the south of the Equator. The heated air rises, sucking moisture from the oceans and generating huge cumulus clouds that produce thunderstorms. This gives the rainy season in the southern hemisphere, when tropical cyclones – hurricanes and typhoons – are at their most active.

Calcutta (India)

Rainfall (mm)

1600mm

J F M A M J J A S O N D

Temperature (°C)

18°C

J F M A M J J A S O N D

The Indian monsoon

The Indian subcontinent experiences a special kind of tropical climate triggered by the shape of the land. This huge triangular subcontinent is bordered by the Indian ocean to the east, the Bay of Bengal to the west, and the world's highest mountains – the Himalayas – to the north.

India is coolest in December, but the Indian ocean and the Bay of Bengal are still warm. Air sinks over the cool land and flows out to the oceans. No moisture flows onto the land, and this produces the dry season.

By April, the Sun is back in the northern hemisphere. Skies over India are still clear, allowing the full strength of the Sun to heat the land. During May, the air gets hotter and hotter. This is the hottest time of the year. It is regularly over 40°C, and in the heat tempers can fray. Everyone looks forward to a break in the weather and a flow of colder, moist air from the ocean. But only in June does it become hot enough to reverse the flow of air from land to sea.

The change is particularly dramatic over India. Air rushes in from the oceans, changing from clear skies to rain in a matter of a few days.

❐ (left) The rainy season at Calcutta, India (Location: 23°N;88°E), begins fitfully in May, but by June rain is falling each day. Clouds during the monsoon help to moderate the temperature, so that the middle of summer is not the hottest time of the year.

❐ (below) The poor suffer most during the monsoon. Because they have to build on easily-flooded land, their settlements are often flooded for weeks on end.

❐ (above) The farming year is controlled by the monsoon season. Seeds are planted and crops grow in the rainy season, then ripen in the dry season that follows.

❐ (above) Calcutta in July. In the midst of the rainy season it is common for the streets to be flooded due to the very heavy rainfall.

Sahara and the deserts of the Middle East and Australia are examples of this kind of desert.

Dry climates also occur in the centres of the continents, simply because they are so far from the moisture-bearing winds that they receive only small amounts of rainfall. The Gobi Desert of Asia is of this kind.

Some dry climates also occur in regions that shelter behind large mountain ranges such as the Andes and the Rockies. The deserts of Nevada, California and Arizona in the United States and the Patagonian Desert of Argentina are of this kind.

Finally, dry climates may occur close to the coast where hot dry winds always blow from the land, rarely from the sea. The Atacama Desert of Chile, Baja California in Mexico, and the Kalahari Desert of Namibia, are examples.

In some cases there is more than one cause for dryness. Such places are the driest places on Earth.

Dry climates have hot summers with no reliable rainy season. Rainfall is always far too low for all but the most specialised plants to survive.

Desert climates are called arid climates. Along their margins are regions which get a short, unreliable wet season, whose climates are collectively called semi-arid, although they are also known by names such as steppe (see page 50), bush and prairie. The dry savanna (semi-arid thorn scrubland) lies on the side closest to the Equator of the main deserts. The largest area is known as the Sahel, and it stretches to the south of the Sahara Desert. It is one of the places where hundreds of millions of people try to grow subsistence crops against all the odds. The Sahel has experienced devastating droughts between 1912 and 1915, 1941 and 1942, and worst of all between 1968 and 1974). Each time the disaster is greater because its population is growing fast.

Savanna Climate

Examples: East Africa, much of Brazil, inland India, Indochina, Northern Australia.

All months have average temperatures above 18°C and a range throughout the year of less than 18°C

Between the rainforests and the deserts, all areas have a wet and a dry season. For several months there may be almost no rain at all, then for several months thunderstorms will occur on many days.

These lands change dramatically with the seasons. In the dry seasons they are parched and brown, trees lose their leaves and the grasses wither until they appear to be dead. The scrub becomes as dry as tinder.

Then, as the seasons change, storms begin to build and lightening flashes may set the dry land on fire. Finally, the storms bring rain and the land begins to come alive as plants grow and leaves burst forth, turning the landscape green again.

This savanna climate, named after the open grassland/woodland vegetation that occurs there, can be a very productive region for farmers. But towards the deserts the dry season gets longer and the rainy season less reliable, and the chances of crops failing become very high. In these places, people often live on the verge of disaster.

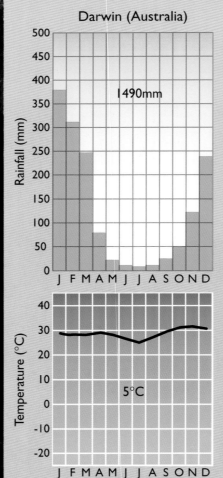

Darwin (Australia)

1490mm

5°C

☐ (left) Darwin, Australia (Location: 13°S;131°E), lies in the savanna belt close to where the climate changes to tropical rainforest. There is a dramatic change in the amount of rainfall throughout the year although temperatures remain steadily high.

The Australian savanna (bush)
A huge "boomerang"-shaped area of Australia is covered by savanna woodlands. The region almost encircles the arid centre of Australia. Most of the area receives rainfall seasonally, with a long dry season in winter in the north of Australia and a long dry season in summer in the south. The main types of tree found in the zone are stunted eucalyptus,

□ (below) Natural grasslands of the African savanna also contain some trees, such as the deciduous acacia tree shown here. Many animals cope with the long dry season and lack of grazing land by migrating. Their migrations, like that in East Africa of animals like the wildebeest, are the greatest on Earth.

Harare (Zimbabwe)

830mm

8°C

□ (above) Harare, Zimbabwe (Location: 18°S;31°E), is a part of the dry savanna. The temperatures are moderate because Harare is on a high plateau.

□ (left) People cope with the long dry season in many ways. This picture of savanna lands in Kenya show the dusty ground. People store food until the wet season allows replanting, and they try to conserve water in small reservoirs and stone jars. The lack of water makes these people extremely efficient at using this vital resource.

Both arid and semi-arid climates are so dry that trees are found only near rivers or where spring water rises to the surface (an oasis). Plants that grow in these regions reflect the amount of rain that falls. The rule is, the drier the climate, the more woody the plants; the wetter it is, the more grasses thrive.

Dry mid-latitude steppe and prairie climates

The centres of the great continents are plainlands. In the Americas, Australia and Asia these areas are far from the sea and are sometimes also cut off from moisture-bearing winds by high mountains. The driest areas are deserts, but much of the land is covered with natural grasslands that are called steppes in Asia, prairies in North America, and pampas in South America.

> **Deserts can be**
> • in the centre of a continent
> • in places where hot air is always sinking;
> • in a rainshadow of high mountains; and
> • in places where the winds always blow offshore

These mid-latitude semi-arid zones have some things in common with the tropical savanna regions (of which the Australian bush is an example), but they also have many contrasts. For example, both regions have a wet season of low, unreliable rainfall, often in the form of torrential thunderstorms. Like the dry (thorn) savanna, the steppes may have several years with good rainfall followed by several years of drought.

This natural cycle of rainfall in the prairies of the United States caused the great disaster of the Dust Bowl. Native Americans, having long experience of this land, were mainly nomads because they knew they couldn't rely on it as cropland. The first Europeans labelled this land the Great American Desert. Yet new

Arid and semi-arid climates

Examples: Sahel of Africa, Iraq, Iran, Namibia, interior Australia.

The rainfall average is usually below 50 mm a year in arid regions, below 300 mm in semi-arid regions. Rainfall is very unreliable.

In all arid and semi-arid regions, clear skies allow temperatures to soar in the day (when the Sun shines) and fall dramatically during the night (when the heat is lost to a cloudless sky). In the Sahara Desert, temperatures sometimes vary by over 50°C from day to night.

Rainfall is very low and very unreliable. In deserts there may be no rain for years and then a sudden downpour of hundreds of millimetres of rain that will cause flash flooding.

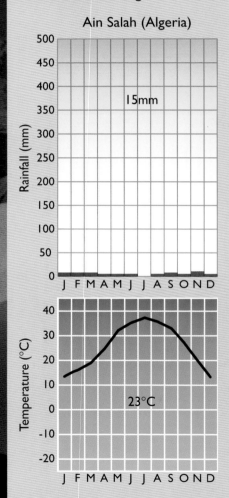

Ain Salah (Algeria)

15mm

23°C

❏ (main picture) Lack of water means that little vegetation protects the surface from wind action. This allows the wind to form loose materials into features such as sand dunes. This is Death Valley, California, a rainshadow desert.

❏ (left) Ain Salah, Algeria (Location 27°N;2°E) is one of the world's driest places. Deep in the Sahara Desert, it experiences rainfall only occasionally. Years without any rain may be followed by a torrential downpour and flooding. For this reason, the rainfall averages shown in this chart do not show a pattern that can be expected every single year. Notice that the temperature range is very high, with summer temperatures of nearly 40°C contrasting with cool winters of just 12°C.

❏ (right) Dry scorching winds require special kinds of clothing. Arab people dress in loose clothes that can be rearranged to cover the face during duststorms. This is a traditional way of dealing with such a harsh climate.

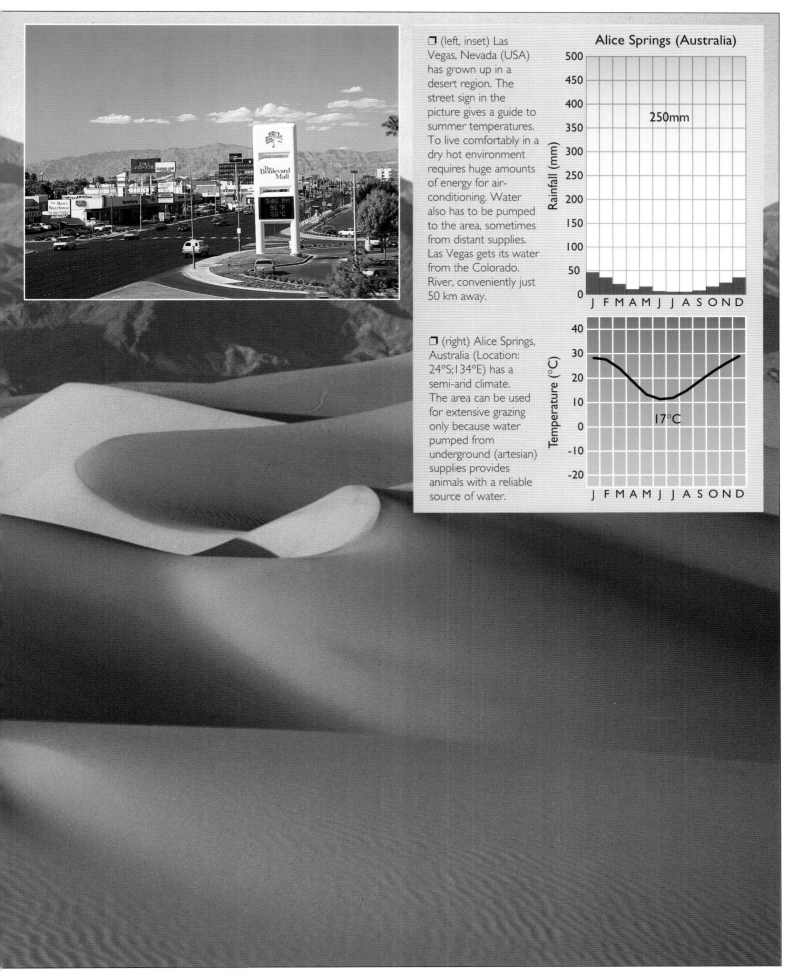

□ (left, inset) Las Vegas, Nevada (USA) has grown up in a desert region. The street sign in the picture gives a guide to summer temperatures. To live comfortably in a dry hot environment requires huge amounts of energy for air-conditioning. Water also has to be pumped to the area, sometimes from distant supplies. Las Vegas gets its water from the Colorado. River, conveniently just 50 km away.

□ (right) Alice Springs, Australia (Location: 24°S;134°E) has a semi-arid climate. The area can be used for extensive grazing only because water pumped from underground (artesian) supplies provides animals with a reliable source of water.

Alice Springs (Australia)

250mm

17°C

immigrant settlers from the east did not understand the problems that this climate brings and they began to plough the soil. All was well for a few years until the dry years began.

You can see how regular the cycle of good and bad rainfall years may be by noting the years when farming was a disaster: the 1890s, then the 1910s and then again the 1930s were the worst years of all.

In this last period, the winds that blew over the ploughed land carried away so much topsoil that it coloured the sky as far as the other side of the continent.

Disasters are only avoided today by using irrigation water and methods of farming that conserve soil moisture.

The real difference between the dry savannas and the steppes is not so much felt in summer – both regions have temperatures that reach a ground-baking 40°C – but in the winters. In the mid-latitudes, cloud-free skies allow the ground to lose heat and the land gets colder and colder.

Winter temperatures of –40°C are commonplace in the Asian steppes and the North American prairies, where flat, treeless lands offer no barrier to the winds. A combination of low temperatures and strong drying winds that blow for weeks on end makes it especially difficult to survive these areas in winter. The harshness of the climate is one reason why so few major cities are to be found in the centres of continents. Most people simply do not want to live in these unattractive places.

> Semi-arid climates pose some of the greatest problems for both farmers and city dwellers. No one can rely on the rainfall, so supplies must be tapped from underground rocks or brought by canal from distant places with a water surplus.

Steppe and prairie climate

Examples: Steppes of Russia, Great Plains of North America
Rainfall too low for trees to grow except by watercourses, temperature varies greatly between summer and winter and from year to year.

The prairies of North America are lands of great extremes. Summers are sunny and hot with frequent afternoon thunderstorms and the chance of tornadoes. Winters are cold with no more than a sprinkling of snow.

The steppes and prairies also have a climate that seems to go in cycles. There may be a decade of good rains followed by a decade of drought. This is what makes the steppes and the prairies so difficult for farmers, and a reason why there are so few big cities in the steppes and prairies.

Traditionally, in order to cope with this difficult climate, native peoples were nomadic. Now some of the difficulty is eased by the use of groundwater supplies, or water diverted from rivers.

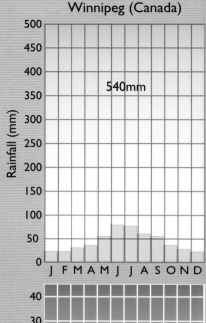

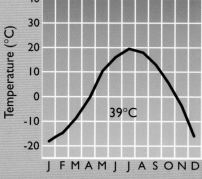

❑ (above) Winnipeg (Location: 50°N; 97°W) is in the heartland of the Canadian prairies. Being more northerly than Denver, the winters are colder, although summers are similar.

Denver (USA)

Rainfall (mm)

360mm

J F M A M J J A S O N D

Temperature (°C)

23°C

J F M A M J J A S O N D

◻ (above) This picture shows how the use of irrigation can transform the land from poor grazing to a rich circle of cereals.

◻ (main picture and right) Denver, Colorado, USA (location: 40°N;105°W) is the 'capital' of the Great Plains, the high plateau steppelands of North America.

Humid mid-latitude climates

The humid mid-latitudes, are regions where certain characteristics of both the climates of both the tropics and the cold lands are mixed. Those nearest the tropics (places such as Florida (USA) and coastal New South Wales, Australia, which are called subtropics) have near tropical summers, but changeable winters; those closer to the poles (places like New England, (USA), United Kingdom and Western Europe and South Island, New Zealand) have changeable weather throughout the year.

The mid-latitudes are, however, especially influenced by swirling masses of cloud and rain called depressions. This is quite different from the tropics and the dry regions, whose rain is mainly in the form of severe thunderstorms.

> The humid subtropics have warm, sticky summers, but their mild, drier winters make them especially attractive for winter holidaymakers.
> In autumn there is always the risk of hurricanes and typhoons.

The west coasts of the northern hemisphere and the east coasts of the southern hemisphere have the most moderate temperatures in the mid-latitudes. This is because they are greatly affected by warm ocean currents such as the Gulf Stream (also known as the North Atlantic Drift) in the North Atlantic Ocean, and the North Pacific Current. In the southern hemisphere, the Brazil Current and the Southern Equatorial Current have the same warming effect. Air blowing over this warm water is also warmed, thus keeping the winter temperatures mild.

The opposite sides of the continents do not have the advantage of the warm ocean current,

Subtropical (warm temperate) climate

Examples: Southern US states, New South Wales.
Rainfall evenly spread throughout the year with periods of high humidity when tropical air flows into the region and periods of cold "bursters" when winds arrive from polar regions.

The subtropical regions share some of the features of the tropics and the mid-latitudes. They get their summer, tropical, influences (and the Trade Winds) from the east, and their winter influences (and the Westerlies), and its much more changeable weather, from the west.

This change in wind direction means that places on opposite sides of the continents have very different types of weather. Those on the western margins have a Mediterranean Climate (see next page). Those on the east (described on this page) have rain in summer as well as winter. In summer and autumn they are often hot and 'sticky'.

Hurricanes and typhoons are most common in the eastern margins of the subtropics. They may occur throughout the summer, but especially in late summer and early autumn in the Gulf of Mexico and along the coasts of China, Japan and northeastern Australia. (See page 24 for more details.)

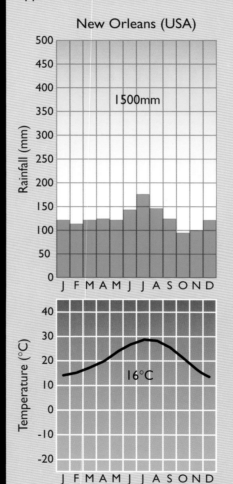

❏ (above) New Orleans (Location: 30°N 90°W) lies near the mouth of the Mississippi river. It receives more rain in summer than at any other time of the year, and at this time temperatures are around 30°C, making it unpleasantly muggy.

Winters are much cooler, but there is always a chance that cold air will be pulled in from the north, giving winds known as Northers in nearby Texas. Cold blasts of air are particularly feared by farmers in the Gulf Coast states because they can kill the blossoms on fruit trees.

❐ (below) Sydney (Location: 34°S 151°W) has a warm temperate climate with a fairly even distribution of rainfall throughout the year.

Unlike most parts of Australia, Sydney receives more rainfall than the amount of moisture that evaporates from the same area. Because Sydney is located on a narrow coastal plain between the Pacific Ocean and a range of mountains called the Great Divide, it also receives relief rainfall from winds blowing onshore.

Although Sydney receives over 1180 mm average rainfall each year, it has relatively few wet days – on average Sydney has fewer than 60 wet days each year. When Sydney receives rainfall, it usually comes through the action of cold fronts or thunderstorms.

By world standards, temperatures in Sydney do not change greatly from season to season. This is because the city is located beside a warm ocean current. The ocean also moderates the temperature, providing welcome cooling in summer and raising temperatures in winter.

Sydney gets most of its rain in autumn, making the climate unpleasantly muggy at this time of the year. By contrast, spring is a much fresher season. Although in summer, especially November and December, it is normally hot, there is always a chance of a sudden cold blast of wind from the south, known as the "Southerly Burster", and temperatures may fall by 10°C in a few minutes.

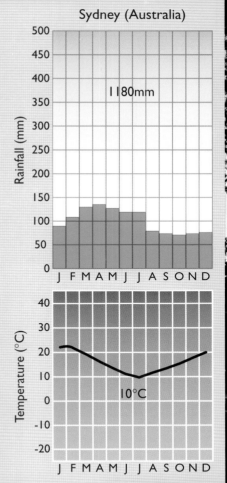

Sydney (Australia)

so during their winters, temperatures can plummet below freezing. Summers are also hotter, and moist air coming from the nearby oceans feeds violent thunderstorms. This is easy to see looking at opposite sides of the Atlantic Ocean, where England has a mild west coast climate, but New England, USA, experiences an east coast type of climate, with hotter summers and colder winters.

Some areas are influenced by depressions throughout the year, bringing rain in every season. Western Europe, southeast Australia, and the area comprised of the northwest United States and southwest Canada are like this. Some areas experience depressions and rain only in the winter, allowing sunny skies and high temperatures in summer – the shores of the Mediterranean Sea and places like California have this kind of climate. Other areas have wet summers and dry winters – for example northern India and much of China.

> Mediterranean lands have attracted many people this century as they seek sunshine resorts or, because they have mild winters, as places to retire. Now many businesses are also moving to these areas, hoping in this way to attract workers.

The jet streams

The weather in the mid-latitudes often seems a chaotic mixture of fine and then rainy weather. Weather forecasters sometimes find it impossible to predict ahead even for a few hours. But scientists have now discovered that the depressions and anticyclones that give such variable weather are steered by fast-moving invisible tunnels of air that move snake-fashion around the globe high in the air. These tunnels of air are called jet streams.

Mediterranean climate

Examples: Southern France, Greece, California, Perth (Australia).
Regions where the coldest month is below 18 °C but above -3 °C. The average temperature of the warmest month is over 10 °C.

This is a warm temperate climate with a dry, sunny and warm summer and a cooler, wetter winter. The Mediterranean Climate only occurs on coasts and it occupies a very small part of the world.

Mediterranean climates are world famous as summer holiday destinations. In Europe, they are also popular in winter because the climate is milder than farther north.

Places with a Mediterranean climate rely on the influence of the cool sea during the summer. Air sinks over the sea and the nearby land, so clouds rarely form.

The opposite effect occurs in winter, when the sea is warm and moist air can flow into the region, bringing rain. In the regions bordering the Mediterranean Sea, depressions reach the region in winter, bringing bands of rain that are similar to the rest of Europe.

The Mediterranean Sea is unique; other places that have a Mediterranean climate, such as California and the area near Perth, Australia, owe their summer sunshine to cold offshore currents, not an inland sea.

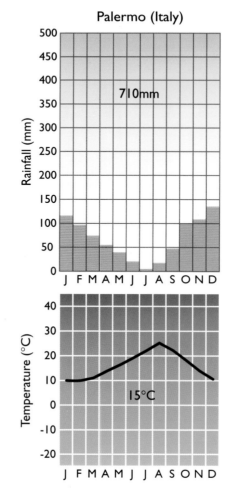

Palermo (Italy)

710mm

15°C

◻ (left) Palermo, Italy (Location: 38°N;13°E) lies on the northern tip of the island of Sicily. In the summer, the influence of the cool Mediterranean Sea means that the island experiences cloudless skies and almost no rainfall. However, as winter approaches the influence of the sea is less, and depressions track along the Mediterranean Sea, producing winter rain. Notice that winters can also be quite cool.

❏ (right and below) Land of colour contrasts. The vegetation of the Mediterranean regions closely reflects the amount of rain that is available. In the winter the land is emerald green; in summer it is a parched straw brown.

These pictures are of the Napa Valley, California. The Mediterranean climate is ideal for growing fruit, but the demand for water during the spring and early summer is high. Because the climate provides rain only in the winter, this water has to be obtained from reservoirs and underground supplies.

In areas with a Mediterranean climate that are not fortunate enough to have piped water, such as much of southern Italy, the only alternative is to plant drought-tolerant crops such as olives.

❏ (below) San Francisco (Location 38°N;122°W) is on the coast of California. Here, the cooler cloudy and wet days occur between October and March. At this time of the year, the grass grows and the hills near the city turn bright green. When the summer sets in, and hardly any rain falls, the grasses die back and the land turns a parched brown.

San Francisco owes its climate to a cold offshore current. It also gives one other special feature for which San Francisco is famous: its summer fogs.

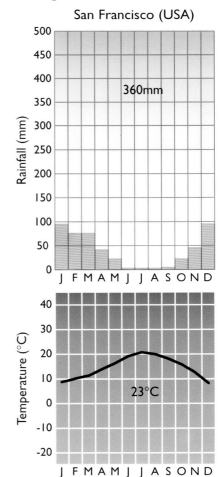

San Francisco (USA)

360mm

23°C

Airline pilots know about jet streams, because their fierce winds have to be avoided; weather forecasters look at them to get a simple picture of what might be going on nearer the ground.

The battle between cool and warm air

In the mid-latitudes, there is a continual battleground between cool air flowing from the poles (or, in winter, from the cold hearts of the continents) and warm, moist air flowing from the tropics. Where these quite different kinds of air meet they swirl together to produce circulating patterns of cloud and rain called depressions.

Because depressions bring together several types of air, each one is unique. This is what makes predicting the weather so hard for weather forecasters.

Each type of air has its own pattern of temperature and moisture which has been created during its journey over land or sea. For example, warm air moving towards the poles gives clear skies and warmer conditions. On the other hand, the clear, dry, cold air that lies over the snow-covered heart of Canada during winter, often flows southeast over the warm ocean currents of the Gulf Stream. This heats the air and gives cloudy skies. Similarly, the cold south wind blowing from Antarctica towards New Zealand is changed as it flows over the warm waters of the South Pacific. This is the air that will eventually produce the cool, rainy days for which the South Island is so well known.

When cool and warm air meet, the warm air is forced up over the cool air and a depression is created (see page 58).

> **Mid-latitude weather is steered by high-level winds called jet streams. The pattern of the jet streams decides the temperatures near the ground.**

Cool temperate rainy climate

Examples: Northwestern Europe; South Island New Zealand; British Columbia, New England.

The mid-latitudes between 40 and 60 degrees are dominated by the passage of depressions and anticyclones, driven by jet streams in the westerly winds. Rain occurs evenly in all seasons.

There is an important contrast between the east and west margins of the continents, just as in the subtropics. In this case, the contrast is because of the warm ocean currents crossing the Atlantic and Pacific Oceans. Westerly winds bring moist mild air across the regions, and there are only short spells without rain. In turn, this makes the areas very green, making them famous as the best pasturelands in the world.

By contrast, eastern margins of continents have much hotter summers and colder, snowier winters.

Thus, while Hudson's Bay in Canada, is snow-covered for most of the year and the ground below the surface remains frozen, Oxford, in England but at the same latitude, has only a few days of frost each year.

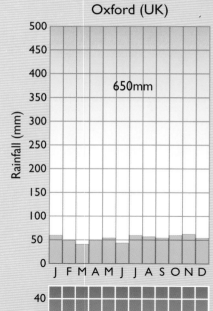

Oxford (UK)

650mm

❏ (left) Oxford, England (Location: 52°N;1°W) has an even pattern of rainfall throughout the year, brought by a constant stream of depressions. The influence of the North Atlantic Drift means that winters are mild and summers remain quite cool. Compare this chart with New York opposite.

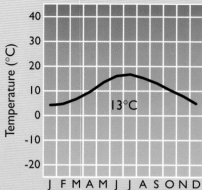

13°C

❏ (main picture) The rapid change in temperature between summer and winter is one of the reasons that trees change colour and lose their leaves so quickly in the New England area of the United States, and the reason why the autumn season is called 'Fall'.

New York (USA)

Rainfall (mm)

1090mm

J F M A M J J A S O N D

Temperature (°C)

24°C

J F M A M J J A S O N D

☐ (above) Many trees in the mid-latitudes are deciduous. This makes the landscape look very different in winter, when trees are leafless and frost lies on the ground.

☐ (above, right) New York, USA (Location: 41°N;74°W) has an eastern margin climate, with a temperature range of 24°C (compared with Oxford's 13°C; see opposite). The hot humid summers contrast with cold snowy winters, and while winter rain and snow falls from depressions, summer rain is much more likely to be due to thunderstorm weather.

☐ (below) Moderate temperatures and rainfall throughout the year allows grass to be grown as a crop in many areas. On the western margins of the continents, it also means that growing and ripening crops is that much more difficult. This is England's Lake District, renowned for high rainfall, green pastures — and no crops.

Humid cold climates

These regions experience a climate that is dominated by a long, dark and bitterly cold winter. They are at their most severe in the centres of the big northerly continents, including much of Russian Siberia.

The natural vegetation of much of this region is coniferous trees. They are able to stand up to the long cold winters when the ground freezes solid. In the drier areas, there is not enough moisture for conifers; instead, tall grasses are found.

Parts of these regions have soil that is permanently frozen (permafrost) just a few metres below the surface. Since the end of the Ice Age thousands of years ago, these areas have simply never been warm enough to allow the soil to thaw.

Polar climates

Polar climates occur over about 12 per cent of the world. In these harsh lands where few people, plants or animals can survive, the average temperature of the warmest month is less than 10°C and all the ground remains permanently frozen.

The 'warmer' parts of this region support vegetation known as tundra, treeless land where only woody shrubs and the hardiest of trees can survive the long winters and the harsh and biting winds that frequently blow. The harshest part, where the temperature never rises above freezing point long enough to allow plants to grow, is barren, snowy and ice-covered.

During the winter, the Sun never rises above the horizon and only a vague twilight occurs. The brightest light is often from the electrical patterns known as auroras.

Highs and lows

The weather in mid-latitudes is caused by sequences of swirling masses of air containing bands of cloud and rain. The pattern is made from regions of high pressure, known as anticyclones, and regions of low pressure, called depressions.

The swirling high and low-pressure regions can be compared with the eddies you see swirling about in a fast-flowing river. Some eddies suck water to the bottom of the river, while others nearby bubble water up to the surface.

In the atmosphere, some eddies suck air upwards (these are the depressions), while elsewhere others swirl air back down again (the anticyclones, or highs). Depressions bring cloud and rain; anticyclones bring clear skies and sunny days in summer, and cold, still, dull or foggy days in winter.

Depressions line up along the boundary between warm tropical air and cold polar air. They are steered by the jet streams.

❐ (below) This satellite image of the UK shows a cold front (the white band of cloud at the right of the picture) just moving away to the east. Cold air with cumulus shower-cloud flows in behind it.

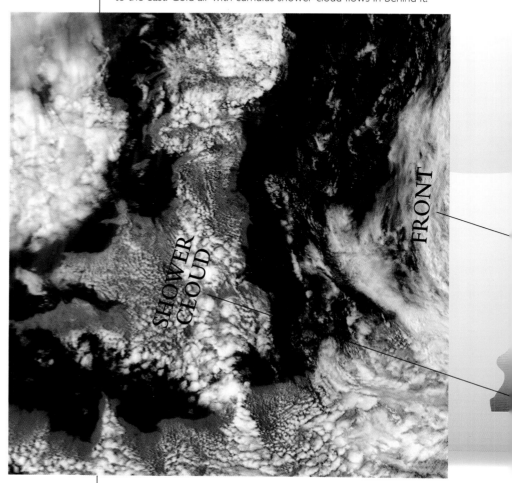

SHOWER CLOUD

FRONT

Depression weather

In a depression, where warm and cold air meet, the less dense warm air glides over the colder air along two sloping zones called fronts. This is shown in the diagram below.

As the warm air rises, it produces thick layers of clouds called stratus clouds (see page 16).

Sometimes you can see a depression arriving. At first the sky is filled with thin, high, wispy (cirrus) cloud (marked A on the diagram below), but gradually, as the first front (called the warm front, marked B) approaches, the clouds become thicker and heavier and rain falls (C).

As the warm front passes overhead the rain stops, the air feels warmer and the clouds thin out (D). This marks the arrival of the warm air.

After a few hours the second front, known as a cold front, passes overhead (E). As soon as the cold front passes, the air suddenly clears and you find yourself in a cold fresh flow of air (F) watching a great wall of cloud moving off into the distance (as shown in the cloud pictures on page 16).

□ (above) The trailing edge of a cold front.

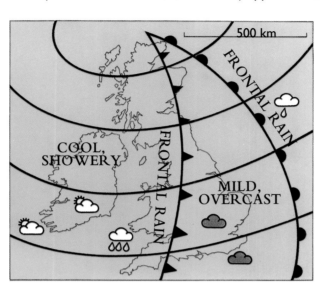

500 km

FRONTAL RAIN

COOL, SHOWERY

FRONTAL RAIN

MILD, OVERCAST

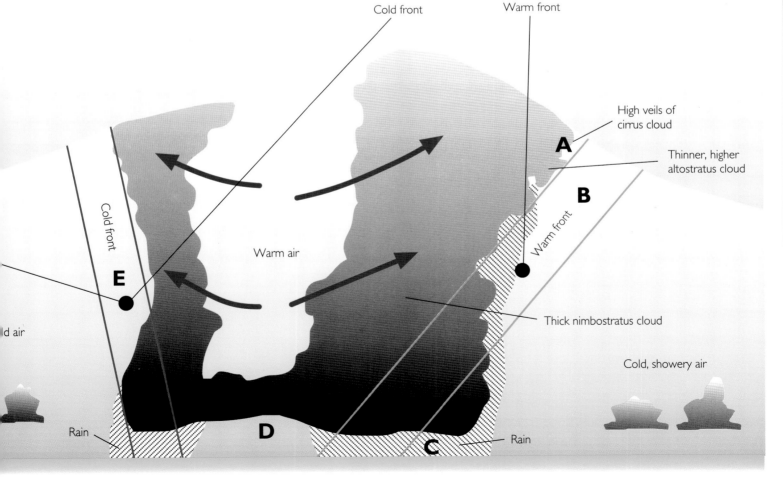

Cold front

Warm front

High veils of cirrus cloud

Thinner, higher altostratus cloud

A

B

Warm front

Cold front

Warm air

E

Thick nimbostratus cloud

ld air

Cold, showery air

Rain

D

Rain

C

With no heat at all from the Sun, the land simply gets colder and colder. Air sinks at the poles and flows outwards, cooling as it moves over the icy lands and producing biting winds that can remain at near gale force for weeks.

Summer is only slightly more hospitable. For months around midsummer the Sun shines constantly, but at such a low angle that it hardly warms the land. Snow and clouds reflect even this meagre heat away.

How the North and South Poles differ

The North Pole is half the size of the Antarctic region; there is little land, and the ice sheet that covers the ocean is thin and almost disappears in summer. Towards the South Pole, the vast continent of Antarctica is covered with ice up to 4000 m thick.

There are differences in the oceans, too. In summer, the Arctic Ocean is affected by the warm waters that flow northwards from the Atlantic (the Gulf Stream), which bring summer moisture and storms. No such warm currents approach Antarctica. As a result, Antarctica is truly the coldest place on Earth. The average temperature for the warmest month at the South Pole is –33°C and the coldest temperature ever recorded is a staggering –88°C!

> The polar climates are special because even in summer the temperature remains below freezing for much of the time. Antarctica in particular suffers from strong winds.

In the Arctic summer, cloud-bearing winds move over the pole, giving it most of its small total snowfall. In Antarctica, storms can usually only reach the edges of the continent, leaving the centre as a true ice desert with clear skies

Weather in cold lands

Examples: Northern North America and Siberia.

The average temperature of the coldest month is below -3°C but the warmest month is over 10°C.

North America, Europe and Asia stretch much closer to the pole than any of the southern continents, and this is why the most northerly regions are the only ones to have cold climates. Exceptions are the northwestern coasts of Europe and British Columbia (Canada). These are kept mild because warm ocean waters stretch along these coasts. But inland, and reaching as far as the eastern shores, the land becomes exceptionally cold in winter, when temperatures may drop to -40°C. By contrast, clear skies and long summer days mean that summer temperatures can be as hot as those in the tropics. After the snow melts, many temporary marshes form on the surface, giving breeding grounds for vast numbers of insects, of which the mosquitos are the most obvious to anyone who visits the areas in early summer.

People who live in these regions experience great changes in their seasons and they can notice the day length and the temperature changing each week.

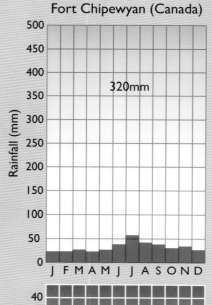

Fort Chipewyan (Canada)

320mm

❑ (left) Fort Chipewyan, Canada (Location: 59°N;111°W) is sub-Arctic Canada. Because it is in the rainshadow of the Rockies, it has a low rainfall. Summer temperatures nearly reach 20°C, but winters are an extremely cold -25°C.

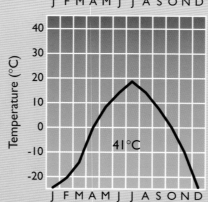

41°C

❑ (far right) Verkhoyansk, Russia (Location: 67°N;133°E) is in the Siberian Arctic. Summer temperatures just rise above 15°C for just 2 months each summer, then plummet to below -40°C.

Verkhoyansk (Russia)

130mm

68°C

for weeks on end. Snow and ice remain thick; in this cold air almost no snow evaporates.

It has now been discovered that each Spring a hole appears in the ozone layer above each Pole. Most scientists believe that this hole is caused by human activities. Although the holes do not directly affect the climate at the moment, the loss of the world's ozone could have vital long-term effects.

Mountain climates

Mountain climates are mosaics of many different local climates that vary with slope, exposure, and altitude. Windward slopes are usually wetter than leeward slopes. In general, temperatures decrease and precipitation increases with altitude, resulting in a vertical zonation of plant life. Seasonal distribution of temperature and precipitation is similar to that of adjacent lowland climates.

❏ (below) Clearing a pass in spring in the Alps. The snow that has fallen during the winter blocks these high passes for over four months of the year.

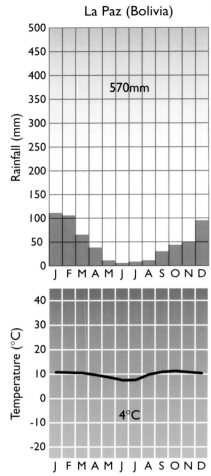

La Paz (Bolivia)

❏ (left) La Paz, Bolivia (Location: 16°S;68°W) is one of the highest cities in the world.

Places would normally be described as tropical at this latitude, and this is seen in the almost constant temperature throughout the year. However, the high altitude means that temperatures are very low, hovering around 10°C (rather than 30°C that would be experienced at sea level).

Glossary

ATMOSPHERE

The shells of gases that encircle the Earth and stretch out for hundreds of kilometres from the Earth's surface. The only shells that affect the world's weather are the lowest shell, called the troposphere, and the shell of gas surrounding it called the stratosphere.

BAROMETER

An instrument for measuring the pressure of the atmosphere. Most common barometers measure pressure change.

CATALYTIC CONVERTERS

These are special exhaust systems installed in modern vehicles, designed to trap many of the exhaust pollutants from an engine.

CIRCULATION

The circulation of the atmosphere is the continual cycling of air between the poles and the Equator. The movement is very complicated because as the air moves it is sent into curling motions by the spinning of the Earth.

DEPRESSION

The word used to describe the swirling mixture of warm and cold air that occurs in the mid-latitudes as air from the poles meets air from the tropics.

DEVELOPING WORLD

Those countries where the majority of people still depend on farming for a living, where wages are poor and where there is a lack of advanced technology such as electricity.

ERODED

When rock and soil slide or are washed away they are said to be eroded.

HAILSTONES

Hailstones are large lumps of ice, made inside the cold, highest regions of a tall thunderstorm cloud.

INDUSTRIAL REVOLUTION

The time during the 18th and 19th centuries when the world first saw automatic machines and steam power. Its most common symbol was the factory.

MIRAGE

The apparent image of a lake or sea that is commonly witnessed over hot land. The effect is due to the special way that light is bent in hot air.

MONSOON

The name for a particular type of wet season in the tropics and near tropics where the rainy season starts very abruptly.

STATISTICS

Statistics are simple numbers used to represent a collection of measurements. The simplest statistic is the average, where all of the measurement values are added and the total divided by the number of measurements.

Further reading

This book is one of a series that covers the whole of geography. They may provide you with more information. The series is:

1. **People** of the world, population & migration
2. **Homes** of the world & the way people live
3. The world's **shops** and where they are
4. **Cities** of the world & their future
5. World **transport**, travel & communications
6. **Farms** & the world's food supply

7. World **industry** & making goods
8. The world's **resources** & their exploitation
9. The world's changing **energy** supplies
10. The world's **environments** & conservation
11. World **weather**, climate & climatic change
12. The **Earth** & its changing surface

Index

Africa 47
air pollution 30
Ain Salah 48
Algeria 48
Alice Springs 49
alto 16
Anasazi Indians 36
Antarctica 60
anticyclones 54, 58
Arctic 60
Arctic Ocean 60
arid climate 46, 48
Arizona 46
Atacama Desert 46
atmosphere 5, 7, 63
auroras 60
Australia 20, 25, 28, 49

Bangladesh 26
barometer 9, 63
barrier islands 25
Belgium 26
Birmingham 28
blizzard 24
Brazil 28
Bristlecone Pine 37
bush 46, 48
bush fire 28
butterfly effect 6

Calcutta 45
California 11, 29, 31, 46
Canada 26, 54
carbon dioxide 7, 38
carbon monoxide 32
catalytic converters 32, 63
China 26, 54
Chinook 8, 18
circulation 6, 63
cirro 18
cirrus cloud 16, 59
climate 6, 35
climate graph 41
climate map 40
cloud 16
cold front 21, 59
cold lands 60
condensation 14
conduction 8
continent 10
continental climate 11
cool temperate rainy climate 56
cumulonimbus cloud 14, 15
cumulus cloud 10, 14, 16, 44

Darwin 46
Death Valley 48
Denver 51

depressions 16, 18, 52, 54, 58, 63
desert 7, 10, 18, 44
developing world 39, 63
disaster 23
Doldrums 9
drizzle 16
drought 24, 28, 36, 46, 48
dry climates 44
dry season 42
Dust Bowl 30, 48

East Anglia 28
Ecuador 28
El Niño 28
England 54
eroded 6, 36, 63
extreme events 23

famine 24, 28
fire 29
flash floods 26, 48
flood 24, 26
Florida 52
Foehn 8, 18
fog 11, 24, 30
Fort Chipewyan 60
fossil fuels 35, 38
French Revolution 37
front 59
frost 18
frostbite 24

Greenhouse Effect 7, 38, 39
Gulf Stream 10, 52

hailstones 13, 63
hailstorm 16
Harare 47
hazard 23
heat transfer 10
heatstroke 24
high pressure 9, 32, 58
humid cold climates 58
humid mid-latitude climates 52
humid tropics 41, 43
hurricanes 12, 24, 44 53
Hwang He River 26
hypothermia 24

Ice Age 36
India 28, 36, 39, 44, 45, 54
Industrial Revolution 32, 63
Ireland 37
isobars 9

jet stream 9, 54, 58

Kalahari Desert 46
Kenya 46
Köppen 41

La Paz 62
lightning 15
Little Ice Age 38

local winds 18
London 32
Los Angeles 32
low pressure 9, 58

Manaus 42
maritime climate 11
Mediterranean climate 54
Mediterranean Sea 54
Mexico City 32, 33
mid-latitude steppe 48
mid-latitudes 7, 48, 50, 52
mirage 10, 63
Mississippi River 27, 52
moisture 12
monsoon 8, 44, 63
mountain 18
mountain climates 62

National Hurricane Centre 32
Netherlands (The) 26
Nevada 46, 49
New England 52, 54, 56
New Orleans 52
New South Wales 52
New York 57
New Zealand 52, 56
nimbostratus cloud 16
nimbus cloud 18
nomads 48
North America 39
North Atlantic Drift 10, 52, 56

oasis 48
ocean 10, 12
ocean currents 10, 52
offshore breeze 8
onshore breeze 8
Oxford 56
ozone 7, 32, 62

Pacific Ocean 28
Palermo 54
pampas 48
Patagonian Desert 46
permafrost 58
photochemical smog 32
polar climates 58
pollution 33
prairie 39, 46, 48

radar 20, 21
radiation 6
rain 13
raindrop 14
rainshadow desert 18, 48
rainshadow region 18
relief rain 18
rime 13

Sahara Desert 44, 48
Sahel 28, 46
San Francisco 31, 55
satellite 20, 21

savanna 46, 48
sea breeze 8, 11
sea level 39
season 12
semi-arid 46, 48
shanty towns 24
Siberia 60
Singapore 43
sleet 13
smog 30, 32
snow 13
snowfall 26
snowflake 14
South Africa 28
statistics 63
steppe 46, 48
stratosphere 6, 7, 8
stratus 16
stratus cloud 16, 59
Subtropical (warm temperate) climate 52
summer 12
Sun 6, 10, 12, 38, 44, 45, 48, 58, 60
Sydney 29

Tahiti 28
thermals 10, 15
thunder 15
thunderstorms 7, 12, 44
tidal wave 25
tornado 9, 20, 25
Trade Winds 8, 44
transpiration 42
tropical cyclone 9, 12, 24, 44
tropical rainforests 42
troposphere 6, 7, 8
tundra 58
twister 25
typhoon 12, 24, 28, 44, 53

ultraviolet radiation 7
United Kingdom 21, 26, 52
United States 21, 25, 26, 46

valley wind 8
Verkhoyansk 61

warm front 21, 59
water droplets 12
water vapour 7, 12, 38
waterspout 25
weather 5
weather chart 20
weather forecasters 54
weather forecasting 18, 20
weather fronts 21
West Africa 28, 44
Westerlies 8
Western Europe 52
wet season 42
wind 7, 9, 10
wind action 48
Winnipeg 50
winter 12

World Geography **People** of the world, population & migration **Homes** of the world & the way people live The world's **shops** & where they are **Cities** of the world & changing **energy** supplies The world's **environment** & conservation World **weather**, climate & climatic change The **Earth** & its changing surface **World Geography** travel & communications **Farms** & the world's food supply World **industry** & making goods The world's **resources** & their exploitation The world's changing **energy** su & migration **Homes** of the world & the way people live The world's **shops** & where they are **Cities** of the world & their future World **transport**, travel & communication & conservation World **weather**, climate & climatic change The **Earth** & its changing surface **World Geography** **People** of the world, population & migration **Homes** supply World **industry** & making goods The world's **resources** & their exploitation The world's changing **energy** supplies The world's **environment** & conservation World live The world's **shops** & where they are **Cities** of the world & their future World **transport**, travel & communications **Farms** & the world's food supply World **indust** change The **Earth** & its changing surface **World Geography** **People** of the world, population & migration **Homes** of the world & the way people live The world's **shop** **resources** & their exploitation The world's changing **energy** supplies The world's **environment** & conservation World **weather**, climate & climatic change The **Earth** of the world & their future World **transport**, travel & communications **Farms** & the world's food supply World **industry** & making goods The world's **resources** & their **Geography** **People** of the world, population & migration **Homes** of the world & the way people live The world's **shops** & where they are **Cities** of the world & their futu **energy** supplies The world's **environment** & conservation World **weather**, climate & climatic change The **Earth** & its changing surface **World Geography** **People** o communicat... **Farms** & the world's food supply World **industry** & making goods The world's **resources** & their exploitation The world's changing **energy** supplies Th **Homes** of the world & the way people live The world's **shops** & where they are **Cities** of the world & their future World **transport**, travel & communications **Farms** & t World **weather**, climate & climatic change The **Earth** & its changing surface **World Geography** **People** of the world, population & migration **Homes** of the world & **industry** & making goods The world's **resources** & their exploitation The world's changing **energy** supplies The world's **environment** & conservation World **weathe** world's **shops** & where they are **Cities** of the world & their future World **transport**, travel & communications **Farms** & the world's food supply World **industry** & m The **Earth** & its changing surface **World Geography** **People** of the world, population & migration **Homes** of the world & the way people live The world's **shops** & their exploitation The world's changing **energy** supplies The world's **environment** & conservation World **weather**, climate & climatic change The **Earth** & its chang & their future World **transport**, travel & communications **Farms** & the world's food supply World **industry** & making goods The world's **resources** & their exploitation **People** of the world, population & migration **Homes** of the world & the way people live The world's **shops** & where they are **Cities** of the world & their future supplies The world's **environment** & conservation World **weather**, climate & climatic change The **Earth** & its changing surface **World Geography** **People** of the world, **Farms** & the world's food supply World **industry** & making goods The world's **resources** & their exploitation The world's changing **energy** supplies The world's **env** of the world & the way people live The world's **shops** & where they are **Cities** of the world & their future World **transport**, travel & communications **Farms** & the **weather**, climate & climatic change The **Earth** & its changing surface **World Geography** **People** of the world, population & migration **Homes** of the world & the way & making goods The world's **resources** & their exploitation The world's changing **energy** supplies The world's **environment** & conservation World **weather**, climate & where they are **Cities** of the world & their future World **transport**, travel & communications **Farms** & the world's food supply World **industry** & making goods & its changing surface **World Geography** **People** of the world, population & migration **Homes** of the world & the way people live The world's **shops** & where they exploitation ...world's changing **energy** supplies The world's **environment** & conservation World **weather**, climate & climatic change The **Earth** & its changing sur futur... World ...sport, travel & communications **Farms** & the world's food supply World **industry** & making goods The world's **resources** & their exploitation The of the world, population & migration **Homes** of the world & the way people live The world's **shops** & where they are **Cities** of the world & their future World **transp** The world's **environment** & conservation World **weather**, climate & climatic change The **Earth** & its changing surface **World Geography** **People** of the world, pop **Farms** & the world's food supply World **industry** & making goods The world's **resources** & their exploitation The world's changing **energy** supplies The world's **env** of the world & the way people live The world's **shops** & where they are **Cities** of the world & their future World **transport**, travel & communications **Farms** & the worl **weather**, climate & climatic change The **Earth** & its changing surface **World Geography** **People** of the world, population & migration **Homes** of the world & the wa & making goods The world's **resources** & their exploitation The world's changing **energy** supplies The world's **environment** & conservation World **weather**, climate & where they are **Cities** of the world & their future World **transport**, travel & communications **Farms** & the world's food supply World **industry** & making goods & its changing surface **World Geography** **People** of the world, population & migration **Homes** of the world & the way people live The world's **shops** & where they a exploitation ...world's changing **energy** supplies The world's **environment** & conservation World **weather**, climate & climatic change The **Earth** & its changing su futur... World ...sport, travel & communications **Farms** & the world's food supply World **industry** & making goods The world's **resources** & their exploitation The of the world, population & migration **Homes** of the world & the way people live The world's **shops** & where they are **Cities** of the world & their future World **transp** The world's **environment** & conservation World **weather**, climate & climatic change The **Earth** & its changing surface **World Geography** **People** of the world, pop **Farms** & the world's food supply World **industry** & making goods The world's **resources** & their exploitation The world's changing **energy** supplies The world's **en** of the world & the way people live The world's **shops** & where they are **Cities** of the world & their future World **transport**, travel & communications **Farms** & the worl **weather**, climate & climatic change The **Earth** & its changing surface **World Geography** **People** of the world, population & migration **Homes** of the world & the wa & making goods The world's **resources** & their exploitation The world's changing **energy** supplies The world's **environment** & conservation World **weather**, climate & where they are **Cities** of the world & their future World **transport**, travel & communications **Farms** & the world's food supply World **industry** & making goods & its changing surface **World Geography** **People** of the world, population & migration **Homes** of the world & the way people live The world's **shops** & where they a exploitation ...world's changing **energy** supplies The world's **environment** & conservation World **weather**, climate & climatic change The **Earth** & its changing su futur... World ...sport, travel & communications **Farms** & the world's food supply World **industry** & making goods The world's **resources** & their exploitation The of the world, population & migration **Homes** of the world & the way people live The world's **shops** & where they are **Cities** of the world & their future World **transp** The world's **environment** & conservation World **weather**, climate & climatic change The **Earth** & its changing surface **World Geography** **People** of the world, pop **Farms** & the world's food supply World **industry** & making goods The world's **resources** & their exploitation The world's changing **energy** supplies The world's **en** of the world & the way people live The world's **shops** & where they are **Cities** of the world & their future World **transport**, travel & communications **Farms** & the worl **weather**, climate & climatic change The **Earth** & its changing surface **World Geography** **People** of the world, population & migration **Homes** of the world & the wa & making goods The world's **resources** & their exploitation The world's changing **energy** supplies The world's **environment** & conservation World **weather**, climate & where they are **Cities** of the world & their future World **transport**, travel & communications **Farms** & the world's food supply World **industry** & making goods & its changing surface **World Geography** **People** of the world, population & migration **Homes** of the world & the way people live The world's **shops** & where they exploitation The world's changing **energy** supplies The world's **environment** & conservation World **weather**, climate & climatic change The **Earth** & its changing future World **transport**, travel & communications **Farms** & the world's food supply World **industry** & making goods The world's **resources** & their exploitation